TEARDROPS
ON MY DRUM

TEARDROPS
ON MY DRUM

JACK ROBINSON

First published in March 1986 by GMP Publishers Ltd,
    P O Box 247, London N15 6RW
Second impression March 1988
World copyright © 1986 Jack Robinson

British Library Cataloguing in Publication Data

Robinson, Jack
    Teardrops on my drum.
    1. Liverpool (Merseyside) – Social life and customs
    I. Title
    942.7'53083'0924   DA690.L8

    ISBN 0–85449–003–5

Cover art by Liz Dalton
Photosetting by M.C. Typeset, Chatham, Kent
Printed in Denmark by Nørhaven A/S

Contents

PROLOGUE

Catslicks and Prodidogs

It was Liverpool on the twelfth of July, the Orangemen's day. Thousands of people filled the city sidewalks. A boy stood on the edge of the pavement. He had arrived very early, anxious to miss nothing. Mounted policemen patrolled the streets, their highly-trained steeds groomed to perfection, leathers shining, harnesses glittering and chains burnished. The snorting animals and their uniformed riders filled the boy with wonder as they trotted and pranced, pushing this way and that to control the crowds.

"When will it start?" thought the boy. "When will they come? Will they ever come? Will I see it all?" Then, in the distance, he saw a banner billowing in the wind, like the great sail on a Viking longboat. It was supported by two large polished oak poles, hand-carved and tipped with brass and gleaming leather. From the tops of the poles came thick silk cords, stretching out to the hands of the other standard-bearers. The main poles were supported in special holster belts, worn proudly by the men marching beneath the wonderful colours and embroidery of the banner.

Then he heard the music. He heard the band and drums, heard the crash of marching feet in perfect step as if trained by a drill sergeant of the Grenadier Guards. The bandsmen's uniforms were immaculate and they held their heads high as they approached the city centre. The tall drum-major tossed his baton high in the air; it was a superb baton, polished oak and silver crested, and every time it fell safely into the quick, white-gloved hands of the drum-major. Then he raised it high and made the long-awaited signal to the big drummers.

The crowd cheered. The powerful arms of the bass drummers bashed away at the quivering pigskin and the noise was thunderous. Big, broad-shouldered men, covered with the skins of tigers, lions and leopards, they would use their muscles for more than drumming before the day was out. As the side-drums and kettle-drums started to tat-a-tat-tat, abusive chants began to fill the air.

Thump! Thump! "Paddy was a bastard!" Thump! thump! "Paddy was a bastard!" Rat-a-tat-tat! "Paddy was a bastard all his life!"

The Catholics in the crowd retaliated loud and clear. "He! Hi! Billy was a bastard! Billy was a bastard all his life!"

The drums drowned the protests and the marching men sang on ... "We are the sons of Billy and to hell with Popery!" King Billy on his white horse screamed out from every banner, as "Catslicks" and "Prodidogs" relived the Battle of the Boyne. The parade came on and on: more men, more bands, more drums. The Netherfield Road contingent, wearing navy uniforms – dry land sailors from "the good ship neverbudge" but no rabble, they were the toughest squad among the Prods. The skirl of the bagpipes warned of the coming of the Liverpool Scottish Regiment, kilted and spatted, with skean-dhus tucked into the tops of their stockings. They were Loyal Orange Lodge and proud of it. Men in bowler hats and business suits sporting the orange sash, veterans from the British Legion, Apprentice Boys, beautiful girls in white silk dresses, the parade went on and on ...

As the tide swept past, a skinny-legged "Mary Ellen", wrapped in her street-trader's shawl, stared vacantly. She was singing to herself an old skipping-rope song: "Mary Ann SHE! Mary Ann SHE! She locked her door and turned the key." Every few minutes she would step into the road and pick up steaming balls of horse droppings, keeping a wary eye open for the police. As she put the droppings into a straw handbag, some people thought she was simple but most knew that she was preparing for the big moment in the parade when a handsome young man would appear on a white horse, the King Billy of the day.

At last he arrived, the replica William III, escorted by six sword-bearing Scots. The crowd gasped, and then they were all singing: "We are the sons of Billy, and to hell with Popery." The boy sang too. He didn't know who Billy was or what Popery was but he knew the tunes – he had heard them all his life. He knew that "Paddy was a bastard" and "Billy was a bastard" and wondered if everyone was a bastard. Were the mounted police on the great black and chestnut chargers bastards?

The emaciated Mary Ellen stepped into the path of the "King". "Shit, she's going to throw the shit at King Billy!" shouted the crowd.

"Shove it down his fuckin' gob!"

"Knock his friggin' 'ead off!"

She put her hand in the straw basket but a half-ton police horse knocked her flat. "Ee Eye Ee Eye Ee Eye O! Ee Eye Ee Eye Ee Eye O! Paddy was a bastard, Paddy was a bastard all his life . . . "

The woman lay in a mess of blood, horse piss and droppings. Two St John's Ambulance men carried her away, her shawl dragging in the gutter. The parade went on to fill the ferry boats crossing the Mersey.

The boy watched them go. Contingents from Toxteth, contingents from Speke and Everton, from every place he had ever heard of. Nurses and chaplains, boy scouts, girl guides, Wigan miners and Warrington brewers, men from Knotty Ash, Tuebrook, West Derby, Prescot and St Helens . . . He had seen enough. He turned and started the two mile walk home. He was tired and hungry, his bare feet were bruised and dirty, but it had been a great day. As he made his way up the hill to London Road, he wondered if there would be any food in the house, if his father would be drunk, if his mother would belt him across the ear for being out all day. At Prescot Street he saw the teams of chain horses waiting at the bottom of the steep hill, ready to link up and help with the heavy carts carrying loads from the docks.

At the bottom of Brunswick Road he saw a single horse, straining under a massive load. The boy looked at the carter who smiled at him, so he began to push with all his might. A dock labourer on his way home from work joined in, then a young man added his weight. They stopped at the water trough outside Grant's Gardens and the horse drank and rested a while. The docker gave the boy a package wrapped in the Last City edition of the *Echo*, and so did the carter. The boy soon had them open. Bread and cheese and pickle, bread and marge and chunks of corned beef. "'Oly Jeezus, it's my lucky day!"

The boy sat on the edge of the horse trough and sank his teeth into the sandwiches. When he had finished eating, he picked up the heavy steel drinking-cup chained to the trough, rinsed it out and filled it from the tap. He was happy and he wasn't hungry. It had been a wonderful day. He ran and skipped the last hundred yards to his miserable home, singing, "My name is Jackie Robbo and to hell with Popery." Tonight he would sleep well beneath the old overcoats that served as blankets, not caring about the fleas which shared them.

CHAPTER ONE

Sweet Smell the City Streets

"Vote! Vote! Vote for Harry Walker! He is the man to fight for us! He's a solid Labour man! We will have him if we can! And we'll throw the other bastards in the dock! At eight o'clock! In the morning!"

The Kazoo band – shabby, worn-out men, flat-capped and mufflered, with mouth-organs, comb and paper, cone-shaped kazoos and penny whistles knocking out the tunes – marched down the street in their faded overalls, dusty down-at-heel boots and baggy trousers.

The intimidating words flew fast and furious. "If you don't vote for him! We will bust your door in! And you'll never see your Daddy anymore!" They carried sticks and cardboard pictures, and slogans that read "Vote for Harry Walker!" One of the men left the filthy gutter, stepped onto the pavement and thrust some leaflets at my dad. "Vote for Harry!" he shouted.

"Go to fucken' 'ell!" said my old man.

"The ale-house is open!" said his mate Billy.

"We'll come knockin' at your door!" sang the dusty bully boys. "If you don't vote for him . . ."

Billy Krilly leaned on his crutch, swung his one and only leg and staggered into the ale-house with my dad.

"Who's Harry Walker?" asked my young friend Doris Green.

"I don't know and I don't care," I replied, "but I like the song."

The ale-house doors swung to and fro. Some of the marchers went inside to wet their whistles and try to recruit a few more marchers for their cause. Most of them just carried on, turned down Brunswick Road and waved their placards at the passing shoppers.

"Should we follow them?" I said.

"No," said Doris. "Come in the jigger with me and I'll show you my bum."

Doris Green wasn't exactly beautiful. In fact, she was quite the opposite. She had straight, mouse-coloured hair, gozzy eyes and an unclean nose. A pair of steel-framed spectacles helped to keep her eyes in focus and a pink ribbon held her long tatty hair in place. I liked her. She was one of the first people in my life, always laughing and showing me her bare bottom.

Her father was a muck-man; he dug the muck from the middens, piled it onto a wheelbarrow and trundled it away to the corporation muck-cart. He was the dirtiest-looking man in the world but he could not do much about that while the residents of our neighbourhood still had middens – ten foot brick wells for throwing muck into.

Some of the more fortunate residents had been supplied with dustbins. They were serviced by the dustmen but unfortunately for Doris's old man, he was too good a muck-man to be considered for promotion to the dizzy heights of bin-man and had to remain in the middens all his life.

Doris didn't seem to care if he was covered in muck or not; when she saw her dad coming home from work she ran to him, arms outstretched, eyes agleam with happiness and hair flowing gently in the slip-stream. The muck-man would pick her up, swing her in a dizzy circle and kiss her gently on the nose.

The stink of the jiggers, that's the very first thing I remember – the jiggers and back entries that separated the mean streets where I played as a child. The overflowing dustbins and the spilled ashes, the eggshells and the mouldering tea-leaves which always seemed to be clinging to my hands and lodged black under my fingernails.

Our house was one of a terrace in Radcliffe Street. There was room enough for my parents, my two sisters and me, but no one thought the kind of people who lived in Radcliffe Street would worry about not having a bath, an inside lavatory or hot water. Ours was a hungry house. My father never worked. The cupboard was bare, and I remember always going to school dirty and barefoot.

I never really knew my parents. Perhaps my mother loved me. I don't know. She never told me. Perhaps my mother would have given me her last penny. I don't know. She never had one. True, she never had much luck but she had a beautiful singing voice and would entertain my father and his friends during a piss-up in the parlour. The parlour was strictly off limits for me; it was a place reserved for funerals, family gatherings, my old man's one-legged mate and the regular visits from the cops.

My father must have loved me at one time because he gave me his first name, but he was a stranger, a drunken man who terrified me. Unfortunately, like most of his generation, he had been through the horrors of the Great War. He would wake up in the middle of the night and scream. He saw rats that did not exist and crawling monsters that frightened the life out of him.

One day he went to the new dog track with my Uncle Johnny. When they returned, Uncle Johnny had my dad's flat cap on his head and my father had Johnny's big soft Fedora pressed to his chest. Dad cleared the dirty dishes from the kitchen table, one sweep of his arm sending the filthy crockery crashing to the floor, and tipped the contents of the hat onto the white wood table. It was full of money! A pile of crumpled notes, a heap of silver coins – two-bob bits, gleaming half-crowns, shiny shillings, spinning sixpenny pieces and hundreds of threepenny joeys. What a sight! It was almost Christmas and the family danced and screamed with delight.

Two days later, the old man gave me a parcel. "Your Christmas present," he said with a smile. What magic gift would I find? A set of gorgeous clockwork trains? A hundred toy soldiers? A fabulous Meccano set? My mum, dad and his pal Billy Krilly stood over me as I opened the box . . . and screamed with horror, fright and bewilderment, running from the house in tears. For the box contained a false leg – a knee joint, a flesh-coloured calf and hip. Jesus – it looked so real! But perhaps he *was* a good man: he'd spent his winnings on a false leg for his war-time comrade.

Next door was Charlie Redmayne's garage. Charlie had a black and grey monkey who was in the habit of getting out and climbing over the roofs. One day as the draymen were delivering to Gregson's Well, the pub just over the way, the monkey was swinging and chattering on the sign over the garage. Charlie, red in the face with frustration, was shouting at it, "Come down, you stupid friggin' gett!"

What was a "friggin' gett"? I didn't know. Just another word to add to my vocabulary. My old man was a drunken sod and he swore, but he would not allow any of the children to swear. Ignorance was no excuse; I used to say "'kinell" thinking it was only an expression. I must have been about ten years old when I found out otherwise.

The kids in the school yard were huddled round looking at something and laughing their heads off. "What's up?" I asked Cowboy Donaghue and Harry Tarleton. Then I saw what all the laughter was about. Two dogs were stuck together, yelping and barking; the crowd of excited kids wasn't helping any.

"They're stuck together," said Harry.

"Why? How?" I wanted to know.

"They've been fucking, that's all – everybody fucks."

Miss Curran, the deputy head, arrived to throw a bucket of water over the animals and we went into class.

After that it was "fuck this" and "fuck that" and "fuck you". I didn't realise it was an obscenity but when I asked my father to give me the "fucking comic" he was sitting on, he went berserk. He pulled off his thick leather belt, a piece of horse harness dating from when he had been a carter, and went for me.

I dived under the dresser, but he still managed to land two or three belts. I scrambled out and started to run round the big kitchen table, littered with dirty plates and cups and cutlery. He got madder as he found there was no way of getting me, and I made a dive for the door. Too late. The old man picked up a big tin of condensed milk and threw it with all his strength. I came to in the Royal Infirmary, my head sliced open at the left temple. "Fuck it," I said. "Fuckin' home sweet fuckin' home." That time I knew I was swearing.

The only other people in my life were the next door neighbours: Joe Brien, his crippled wife and a beautiful boy named Tommy Lawless who had a permanent smile, a head of soft golden curls, and shoes and stockings on his feet. I used to do Mrs Brien's shopping for her and play choo-choo trains in the gutter with the golden-haired Tommy. Tommy did not belong in our neighbourhood. Anyone could tell by simply looking at his bright clean face and lovely expensive clothes; he was staying with his grandmother while his mother and father were overseas.

It must have been springtime, because romance was in the air. I suppose it must have been leap year too. Doris took me by the hand, led me into the dark shadows of the filthy jigger – the narrowest of lanes between the rows of backyard walls – and took her knickers off. "Now you must show me yours," she said, lifting up her grubby white dress, flashing her little pale slit and giving me an eyeful of the first female sex to come my way. It didn't look all that exciting to me, and I don't suppose mine interested her very much, but she wanted to see it anyway. I pulled down my ragged shorts and Doris saw what she wished to see.

Suddenly an airship appeared overhead. We rushed into the main street, stared in disbelief at the fabulous silver Zeppelin soaring silently through the heavens and waved at it. "It's a Zeppelin!" shouted Doris, waving her navy blue knickers at the posh people in the gondola. I couldn't speak. The glorious midday sunshine glanced and gleamed on the sweeping majestic curves. The unbroken lines and death-like silence of the wondrous sight simply took my breath away. Tommy Lawless bumped into me. "It's the Graf Zeppelin!" he shouted excitedly. "Don't be silly," replied our young female playmate. "It's the R101."

Now the horse-drawn muck-cart came trundling noisily down the street. Doris ran into the jigger, pulled her drawers on and ran to meet her daddy. But Tommy assured me that it was the Graf Zeppelin and took me to his grandma's house to show me his picture books. He was my first friend. He was beautiful. He had sparkling blue eyes, a friendly boyish smile and always smelled as if he'd just stepped from the bath-tub.

We would sit in the lobby of his grandma's home and read hundreds of comics: *The Rainbow*, *Chips*, *Funny Wonder*, *The Jester* and a penny version of *Comic Cuts*. As the days passed we became very close. I often mentioned his lovely golden curls, and how nice and fragrant he smelled.

Tommy's grandmother overheard me one day. The next

time she bathed him, she offered to wash my hair. It was wonderful. I tried to keep my hair clean after that and washed it every chance I got, usually with Mrs Brien's scented soap. I dried on her kitchen towel and examined myself in the mirror. Unfortunately, it was impossible to keep my feet clean but as I couldn't see them in the mirror, it didn't seem to matter.

Joe Brien spent most of his life under the Mersey river digging a tunnel. He was a real Irish labourer and when he came home in the evenings he could hardly move because his muscles ached so much. I had to go to the herb shop and buy liniment and camphorated oil for him, so that his wife could rub him down and get his tired muscles ready for the next day's work. There was a herb shop in every neighbourhood and the proprietor, depending on his skill or reputation as a herbalist, treated most of the sick and wounded. People didn't go to the doctor's. They were too scared or could not afford the five shillings fee. If anybody had a nasty wound or injury, they went to the herb shop and bought the recommended remedy.

My local herb shop was in Everton Road. It was like a magician's cave and Brian Mudd, the fifteen year old cow-keeper's son, was the sorcerer's apprentice. It was a beautiful looking shop. The highly polished walnut shelves were packed from floor to ceiling with gleaming jars and bottles of every shape, size and colour imaginable. Liquorice powder, witch hazel, lavender, coriander, peppermint, cloves, nutmeg, cinnamon, aniseed and all the carminatives in the world stood in rows. There were shelves of mercury and chalk, gregory powders from the rhubarb mixed with magnesium carbonates and ginger, golden mercuric oxide for the eyes, jars of gleaming crystals, salts and sulphates, roots from every corner of the world, tree barks and spices of the Indies, resins, balsams and powdered bone, acids, seaweeds and ferns, leaves from the eucalyptus tree and ipecacuanha, the most popular medicine of all. They claimed that ipecacuanha was originally used by Robinson Crusoe on the desert island of Juan Fernandez.

Amongst this awe-inspiring display stood a huge pair of highly polished brass scales and a pill-making machine.

Young Brian Mudd made the pills. God alone knows how many people they killed but the shop smelled very nice indeed. Now they had a new invention that was guaranteed to cure anything: an electric shock machine. You put a penny in the machine, held the two metal knobs and damn near got electrocuted.

Mr Brien was a very nice, hard working man. He read the papers every day, cut all the comic strips out and kept them for me. Pip, Squak and Wilfred were my favourites, along with Rupert Bear and someone called Old Bill who always appeared in a tin hat and talked about a "better 'ole". This refered to some government proposal to have "homes fit for heroes to live in!".

Mr Brien was quite an intelligent man and knew all about government promises. However, he was very down to earth and called a piss-pot . . . a piss-pot. I did not know any other name for the silly looking receptacle and, as we did not possess one in my own home, I called it a piss-pot, just like Joe Brien.

"The bloody handle has broken off the piss-pot," said my neighbour. "Will you go to Woolworth's and buy a new one for me?" Mrs Brien gave me sixpence. I asked Tommy Lawless to come with me, because I was pretty certain that he would have another name for it, and I could not quite find the courage to ask one of the pretty girls in Woolworth's for a tanner piss-pot!

"It's called a 'po'," said Tommy. I still didn't fancy asking for a po or anything like that, so Tommy came along to boost my courage. We'd got as far as Islington Square when the whole world went mad! Thousands of shabby, grey-faced men in flat caps and white mufflers rushed through the streets, screaming, knocking us over and trampling on us. We scrambled into the safety of a basement area and watched the madness develop.

They tore the bricks from the backyard walls with their bare hands, ripped out the iron railings from the nearby buildings, used them as weapons and to pry up the pavements which they smashed for ammunition against the charging mounted police.

Horses and men went down in bloodied tangles. Police helmets rolled at our feet and we trembled with fear. The men fought on! The police formed ranks like soldiers and charged again, and again! We'd found our "better 'ole" and stayed in it as the men fell to the ground, heads split open, legs and arms broken, blood spilling everywhere. "The gun! The gun!" shouted a little man, tearing the railings from our basement hiding place. "When's the gun going off?!!"

A whistle blew! The police re-formed for another bloody baton charge. The shabby-looking men closed ranks and prepared to fight it out. We thought it must be the end of the world . . . Fire engines came on the scene, followed by black marias to cart the men to the cells, and ambulances with nurses to care for the wounded. The city tramcars stopped. Lorry drivers left their vehicles and joined in the fighting, then came a tremendous boom from across the Mersey. The gun, which always sounded at exactly one o'clock, had been fired. The shabby men cheered and the policemen walked off. They had gone on strike along with everyone else.

Then everyone went on a rampage: rushing into the food shops, smashing the windows of the grocery stores and stealing all the food they could carry.

It looked safe enough to venture out at last. Tommy and I walked hand in hand to Woolworth's. A woman was locking one door as we got there so we shot through another. "What the bloody hell do you want?" she screamed. "Go home before you get hurt!"

"I want one of those," I said, pointing at a pile of hand-painted chamber pots.

"Take one and bugger off!" screamed the woman. I chose one decorated with roses and green leaves, wrapped a piece of paper around it and walked home with Tommy. I could have had a lid if I'd known she wasn't going to take the money.

There were times when I thought I lived in the street of horrors, misfits and lunatics.

The next person to the Briens was an old rat-bag who hated kids. She spent all day looking through her front parlour windows and shaking her fists at the children playing in the street. Next door to her lived a family whose daughter spent all her life lying flat on her back in a strange, wickerwork, coffin-like bed on wheels. If it wasn't raining, they shoved her out in the street all day.

Next door to the basket case lived Mrs Woods. She stank like a midden, must have weighed about twenty-five stone and had two sons, one named Reggie (the oldest boy scout in the world) and one named Joey. Joey looked quite normal but if anybody walked past his door, he smashed them over the head with a broomstick and ran indoors to his enormous Mam.

Doris Green and the muck-man were in the next house, along with seven other members of the family, all lads whose ages ranged from six to twenty-one. They were all a bit potty. The oldest one, Jimmy, pushed a hand-cart all over Liverpool, shouting "Aunt Sally! Aunt Sally!" This wasn't quite as daft as it sounds, because Aunt Sally was a liquid detergent. However, the kids, naturally enough, used to follow him round the streets and every time they saw him, they shouted "Aunt Sally!" at the tops of their voices and he chased them. This again would have been quite acceptable but for the fact that he carried a brass knuckle-duster and was known to have used it many times. I thought he was crazy but he managed to make a living, which was more than most people in the neighbourhood could do.

A blonde flapper lived next door to this happy little family. She wore a lot of make-up on her face and worked in Blackledge's Bread and Cakes Shop.

"When you do the shopping for me," said Mrs Brien, "don't go to Blackledge's for the bread and cakes."

"Why not?" I asked.

"Why not!" she screamed. "Because that painted hussy down the street works there! That's why not!"

No one spoke to the woman who lived next door to the painted hussy because she dyed her hair, used make-up, painted her finger-nails, dressed like a film star, smelled of lovely fragrant perfume and played the piano in the "Lousy Lytton".

Next door to the pianist there was a corner shop. The proprietors had a lovely young daughter named Margery Horton and she spent most of her time upside down, hands on the pavement, feet against the wall, showing her knickers and little pointed titties to all the boys.

Right opposite from me lived another family named

Woods. Mr Woods always dressed in army uniform, but he wasn't in the army and he never had been. He marched up and down the street, showed all the local people what a fine handsome soldier he was and then disappeared for a few days. He had the sweetest young daughter in the neighbourhood but she wasn't allowed out of the house, and we only saw her through the window.

Georgie Pike lived over old Mrs Merrigan's sweet shop. No one would go into Mrs Merrigan's shop because everyone said she was a witch and that her cats pissed all over the sweets in the window. The only way to make contact with Georgie was to stand in the street, throw stones at the window and shout. Georgie wore short trousers, long back stockings, great big size ten boots and a heavy growth of bristle on his chin and upper lip. When he spoke, it was like a mouse squeaking. He was a great footballer, fast runner and could play tirelessly from dawn till dusk. I loved playing with him until Joe Brien warned me off.

"Keep away from Georgie Pike," he said. "You're only a child!"

"So is Georgie," I replied.

"Georgie is twenty-nine years old!" said Mr Brien. "He's as mad as a hatter and he's been going to the Tin School all his life." I didn't know what the Tin School was but I made it my business to find out.

Kipper Willis lived next door to the Merrigans' shop. He had a hair-lip, a cleft palate and he could not speak clearly. He was a nice enough kid but we didn't mix with him because we couldn't understand him. Kids are heartless creatures.

I used to swap comics with the kid in the next house, Frankie McLaglin. He was okay but he lived in fear of his crazy Irish dad.

Most of my street friends came from Bright Street, which cut through Radcliffe Street and formed a small crossroads. Jackie Hughes was a beautiful, blond, feminine boy who walked, talked and acted just like a girl. No one played with him. His brother Arthur was a black boy, handsome and tough and one of the best sportsmen in the street. I couldn't understand how one brother could be white and the other black, but it didn't seem to matter and I know it didn't bother

Arthur or his dainty brother.

Once I got smashed over the head by daft Joey Woods so I took the broomstick from him, smashed him over the head with it and scarpered.

Two-ton Mrs Woods came knocking at my door but I was expecting something like this to happen and climbed on top of Charlie Redmayne's garage.

Mrs Woods then started hitting my old lady with the broom. My mother was just as tough as her so she ran into the house, grabbed a broom and fought it out on the pavement while I sat on the roof-top pissing myself laughing. There they were, fighting away like Japanese warriors: cut, thrust, parry and blow! All the neighbours gathered around, the kid in the basket chair got wheeled up for a ringside view, and Mr Woods marched up and down in his uniform. It might have gone on for ever and turned out to be the fight of the century but Mr Brien came out and threw a bucket of water over them.

I was too scared to go home that night so I slept in Charlie's garage. It had been a stable once upon a time and still had a hayloft with lots of nice straw to keep me warm and a friendly monkey who kept me company.

Reggie Woods, the oldest boy scout in the world, decided to seek revenge. He lured me into his back yard and tied me up with his mother's washing line. I had no idea what he had in mind but it was a bit scary. He definitely had a slate missing. Fortunately, Georgie Pike, the twenty-nine year old school kid came to my rescue; he climbed over the back wall, shoved the daft boy scout into the lavatory and untied the ropes that bound me.

"Come and play running round the block with me?" he asked in his squeaky, high-pitched voice. "I've got a tennis ball in my pocket. We can play catch as we run. No one else will play with me."

"They must be daft!" I replied, catching the ball and throwing it to the happy kid. "Why do they call your school the Tin School, Georgie?"

"Because it's made of tin!" shouted Georgie. "Everybody knows that!" He was the happiest kid in the world.

Billy Wallace had been a high-ranking police officer in the

Liverpool city force. Unfortunately for the local cops, he lost his fine position and they lost a good man. He was fired because he'd joined the General Strike.

Billy Wallace had plenty of money, an outstanding personality and the foresight to take over Gregson's Well, a wonderful-looking hotel which stood on the corner of Brunswick Road and Radcliffe Street and backed up onto Gregson Street. Mr Wallace could quite easily have taken over another equally famous and ancient hostelry called the Coach and Horses but he chose the Well because just across the road was the Royal Hippodrome theatre where all the rich and elegant ladies for miles around went.

As my parents also spent most of their evenings in the Well, they had no idea as to my whereabouts. I used to hang around the bright lights of the Hippodrome, pick up the discarded chocolate boxes and smell them, burying my nose in the lovely wrappers. A smell was almost as good as a taste! If I found a really good one, I would take it home, put it under my pillow and sniff it all night long.

Billy Wallace had two sons: one about my own age named Frankie, and one a little older named Billy. Frankie and Billy enjoyed the services of a couple of servants and their own personal maid, and had a well furnished playroom with clockwork train sets, boxes of gorgeous hand-painted toy soldiers, great big fluffy teddy bears and two enormous rocking-horses. Nevertheless Frankie and Billy were two good, down-to-earth Liverpool kids. My little hovel was only about twenty paces from the Well, and the lads used to shout hello and good night to me every time they saw me pass by.

Billy senior looked and dressed like a wealthy gentleman but he raised not the slightest objection when his fine young sons invited me into their playroom. They might have had wonderful full-sized leather footballs, real cricket bats and big padded boxing gloves but they were not allowed out to play with them. Apart from the daily trip to the posh school they attended, they were in effect prisoners in their marvellous home.

I lived just across the road, could play football as well as Dixie Dean but never had a football in my life. I had to make my own footballs out of old newspapers – dozens of them wrapped tight round a tennis ball and tied with thick pieces of twine. This made a reasonable ball that would bounce and last halfway through a game. By the time it reached the tatty stage, some other kid would have produced a new paper ball and we carried on playing.

I liked the Wallace boys. I felt sorry for them because they were prisoners. They envied me my freedom, thought I had the world at my dirty feet and would have swapped all their teddy bears and rocking-horses for my games of kick-the-can and a climb onto Charlie Redmayne's garage roof to play with his monkey. Unfortunately, they could only watch. Life was good to me in one respect, but there were times when I would have swapped my freedom for a good dinner.

There were still people walking around who remembered the Crimean War, the Battle of Balaclava and the Charge of the Light Brigade. But a guy named Lindbergh had crossed the Atlantic in a small monoplane called "The Spirit of St Louis". Lawrence of Arabia was hiding out in the Air Force under an assumed name, running about the countryside on a motor-bike and raking in the cash from his best-seller *The Seven Pillars Of Wisdom*.

The world was changing all around me; motor cars appeared on the streets and joined the steam-driven lorries and coal-fired traction engines; Al Jolson made the first talking picture and the cinemas in Liverpool got geared up for sound. My mother said she'd cried when she heard Jolson sing "Sonny Boy", so I ran out of the house before she started again and asked me to climb upon her knee . . .

Goods appeared in the shops at ridiculously low prices; a few coppers per week would buy anything on the weekly credit system or the "never never" as it was called by the thousands of people who furnished their homes for a couple of shillings, scarpered to a new address and never never paid.

Ordinary families could get dental treatment for the price of one penny, which they dropped into a turnstile slot at the Liverpool free dental clinic. The herb shops changed their name to sarsaparilla stores, sold root beers, malted milk, milk shakes and hot bovril. They became hang-outs for the local teenagers and stayed open until midnight to catch the late cinema crowds and youngsters from the jazz halls.

Liverpool was catching up with the rest of the civilised world, but no one seemed to be able to get rid of the dreadful fog. The fog was a curse! I knew that nothing would ever shift it. It was so thick and dense in the mornings that I found it impossible to make my way to school without holding onto the buildings, feeling my way and counting my steps exactly like a blind man. People bumped into each other, traffic went on the wrong side of the road and crashed head on with other vehicles. The gas lamps made it worse, especially when you smashed into them with your forehead.

CHAPTER TWO

The Patron of Lost Causes

It was around the time of the General Strike that I started school, an old-fashioned establishment called St Jude's. School! I loved it!

"Jackie boy!"

"Master?"

"Sing ye well?"

"Very well!"

"Hey down!"

"Ho down!"

"Derry derry down . . . among the leaves so green O!"

That was my first lesson: all the ragged-arsed kids singing their heads off. It wasn't much of a school but the singing was beautiful. The Headmaster led the singing lessons, waving a tiny white baton and making us pause for the correct timing:

"I cleaned the windows so successfully . . . one two three four five six seven . . . that now I am the ruler of the King's Navy!"

The Headmaster was magnificent and could produce beauty from our childish throats. He was also kind enough to present me with two wonderful leather-bound books: first prize for reading and first prize for composition. They were the most beautiful books in the world: engraved in rich gold letters and every single page with a fine edge of gold. They were my first possessions and I adored them!

Running home from school, I showed them to my mother. "Look at my prizes!" I said proudly. "Grimm's Fairy Tales! Robin Hood! I won them! They're mine!"

"Hmmm!" replied my mother. "I'd better put them in a safe place for you."

I was not to see them again until I was well past my sixth

birthday. At that time there was a second-hand comic shop in Everton Road. If a child gave the shopkeeper ten old comics, he could choose five comics in exchange or buy ten comics at half the normal price.

Tommy had brought a bundle of comics from his grandma's home and we visited the comic shop. We looked in the window to see the display and there, before my very eyes, were the two beautiful leather-bound books I had won during my first six months at school.

"They're mine!" I said to the man in the shop. "Look in the fly leaf and you'll see my name!"

He looked down at my dirty feet and ragged trousers, smiled and shrugged his dusty shoulders. "They are mine now," he said quietly.

I offered to work for him, and he laughed at me. "What kind of work can you do?"

"Anything!" I replied quite seriously. "Sweep the floor, clean the windows, tidy the bookshelves and sort the comics out for you."

"Save your pocket money up," said the miserable old devil. "I'll keep them for you, and when you've got two shillings you can buy them from me."

Two shillings! He might just as well have said ten thousand pounds!

It was one of the saddest days in my life. The journey home: one foot trailing in the filthy gutter and the other on the pavement's edge, curses running through my head. "Dirty old smelly cow! Fuckin', stinkin' bastard! She sold my books! God blind her!" But it was no good crying. I'd learned that long ago in the filthy home I lived in; the same place I'd learned those same swear words.

I did not let Tommy hear the swearing because I loved him. One day a bright new automobile stopped outside his grandma's house. A handsome golden-haired gentleman stepped from it, and I knew at once that he was Tommy's father. A beautiful modern young lady popped out of the car. She held a long, elegant cigarette holder, blue smoke curling up in rings. They went indoors and Tommy was lost to me forever.

It had been wonderful. I'd learned to love poetry, reading and how to keep my hair fresh and clean. Some of Tommy's gentleness and good manners had rubbed off on me, and I had learned that decent people would accept me.

And there were plenty of other kids to play with, poor and rough like me. I joined them in the street games and could hold my own with any of them. Certainly I missed Tommy's bright golden curls, cheery smiles and all the happy times we'd spent on his doorstep, but the joy of playing baseball in the streets made up for almost anything.

Baseball was my favourite game. A lot of people think that baseball is an American game but they are wrong. My street pals chalked a diamond on the city streets, laid beer sacks full of sawdust down for bases and held up the traffic to make a home run! The carters would stop their horse and wagon rather than spoil a kid from getting to his base; cops chased us, housewives screamed at us but nothing could stop the wonderful enthusiasm of the baseball players.

If the kids wished to play skipping, as opposed to skipping rope individually, then a huge twenty-foot rope was required, stretching from one pavement to the other. Thomas the fruit merchant supplied the rope free of charge. He was glad to get rid of the thousands of woven straw ropes in his cellar. All his staff were kind and friendly, and supplied half the people in Everton with wood from the untold thousands of boxes he handled.

Families did not then have refrigeration: a meat safe was used instead. It looked like a rabbit hutch, had a lightweight frame door with a piece of wire mesh stretched over it, and if you looked closely, you could see beneath the paint and varnish the words: Thomas, Fruit Stores, Brunswick Road. Kids also made home-made carts from his apple boxes, piled the carts with his wood and dragged them through the city streets. The more enterprising ones would chop the wood into sticks, tie the sticks into bundles and flog them door to door. "Firewood! Penny a bundle! Fine dry firewood!"

When the kids stretched the huge ropes across the street to play at skipping, again the traffic had to stop or run them down. Carters waited patiently until we laid the rope flat to prevent the horses from being tripped up. This created many an ambush for the unwary carter who was carrying loads that could easily be stolen: sacks of nuts, brown sugar, delicious locust beans from the carob tree – sweeter than any toffee and as hard as a rock. A sharp knife would easily slit open a sack and every possible receptacle was used to steal the man's goods.

However, there were some carters, wise in the wicked ways of the world, who shouted "Whip behind!" as they drove away. It was a brave kid who would attempt to climb on the wagon then! A twenty-foot whip would crack through the air, making a whistling sound as it lashed the rear of the cart and made the sawdust fly.

Mineral water lorries were a great target with their brightly coloured bottles of pop – Vimto! Tizer! Raspberry, strawberry and every gorgeous drink in the world! I ambushed them regularly. I did not want the pop; I needed the empty bottles. They were worth a penny each and without them I would surely have starved to death. A penny bought me a packet of chips.

On my first day in school after being transferred from the infant's department, I met a boy named Eggy. We were to share a two-seater desk in Standard One. The school had seven classes numbered from one to seven. If we turned out to be bright lads then we would miss Standard Seven and finish up in Standard Seven A, a special class for those with a promising future.

"My name's Jack," I informed him as we sat down.

"I'm Tim," said the boy, "but everybody calls me Eggy."

"Stop talking! shouted Mr Free, and threw a heavy blackboard duster. It hit my desk mate on the shoulder and left a big white chalk mark on his nice blue blazer. "Get out here and clean the blackboard!"

Eggy picked up the wooden eraser, walked to the blackboard and wrote the word Twat! in huge white letters. To the kids in St Jude's this meant a girl's sexual organ.

Mr Free stood with his back to the roaring coal fire, his piercing blue eyes searching among the faces of his new class and his hands behind his back. He wore a smart grey suit, polished brown shoes and a neatly tied bow on his neck. He couldn't see Eggy, which was fortunate for the bright-eyed boy with the curly black hair. Eggy gave the board one final rub and then returned to our desk. A slight murmur of suppressed laughter ran through the class. From that moment on I knew that I was going to like my new desk mate and the rest of the kids at St Jude's.

"Keep quiet!" roared the teacher. He left the warmth and comfort of the glowing coal fire and examined the board, suspecting something. He seemed satisfied, picked up a piece of chalk and wrote the words: Knotty Ash. "How many of you can play football?" he asked. Most of the hands went up.

"How many of you think they are good enough for the school team?" was his next question. All the hands dropped, with the exception of a scaly, pumice-stoned extremity belonging to a bright-eyed lad named Stanley Marsden and the eager hands of myself and my desk mate Eggy.

Mr Free then wrote the words Margaret Street on the blackboard. "How many boys can swim?" he asked. There were about thirty boys in the class and only three hands went up, the same three as before.

"Right! Settle down," said Mr Free. "Margaret Street baths is where you will swim. Those of you who think they are good enough to swim for the school team will receive free passes. That means you can go in any day of the week. How many of you want to train for the swimming team?" A dozen hands shot up and Mr Free allowed a faint smile to grace his thin lips.

"Knotty Ash is five miles from here," he went on. "St Jude's owns a piece of land out there. It is our football and sports training ground. Members of the football team will get a free pass on the tramways and can get out to the training grounds in their spare time.

Cowboy Donaghue raised his hand. "I'm a good footballer," he said. "I'm a good swimmer too, but I have no football boots and I don't have any swimming togs." Mr Free just smiled, wrote down the names of his budding athletes and handed out passes for the tram cars and swimming pool.

Mr Free had two canes. He showed one of them to the class. It was four foot long and made a whistling sound as he slashed it through the silence of the classroom. "This is for those of you who do not pay attention," said the old devil. He then produced his other cane. It was burnt black, hardened at the end and twice as thick as the other cane. He brought it down with a *crash*! The inkwell jumped from its little hole in the wooden desk and a cloud of dust arose. "This is for the bad boys," he smiled, thin lipped. I decided right then and there that I would be a good boy and pay attention to the words of Mr Free.

My new friend produced a packet of sandwiches at lunch time and shared them with me in the playground. "Will you walk home with me after school?" he asked. "I'm going to watch the men flying kites and I don't like going by myself." I'd never taken any particular notice of the kite-flying unemployed and thought it a very childish thing for grown men to do. However, my friend seemed to be a nice lad and I could see no reason to refuse his offer.

He took me to Margaret Street reservoir: a park built high in the sky alongside a gigantic water tower. "Don't go into the lavatory," said my friend. "The last time I was here, a man offered me some money to do something for him."

"What did he want you to do?" I asked innocently.

"I don't know," replied Eggy. "I didn't stop to find out. He scared me so I ran away." We stared up at a tiny dot in the sky.

"Look at that one!" said Eggy. "I bet it would pull you off your feet." A cheery-looking young man about thirty was paying out the string. "You can hold it if you want," he said, offering me the taut white twine. I took the line in my hands and discovered the thrill of kite-flying. It was fantastic! The guy could see the look of surprise on my face, the strain on my arms and knew the kite was pulling me off my feet. He took the kite string from me and returned to his little wooden box-like seat. We strolled around, got quite involved in the flying and spoke to the depressed and shabby men reduced to such childish pastimes. There were hundreds of them; they sat on little home-made stools, rigged up quaint looking kite tails and talked about the kites as if they were aircraft. They were indeed great kites; they were not toys by any means. One of the men had travelled as far as Japan to a kite-flying exhibition. He told us that they sometimes flew kites in Japan that could carry a young man aloft.

When they decided to pack up for the day, Eggy turned to me. "Let's go!" he said. "They'll be here all evening winding up the string. It takes hours. Come along and I'll take you to see the kite man."

The kite man smiled at us when we walked into his workshop in Breck Road. "What do you want?" he asked cheerfully. "Tails? Balls of string? Kite stools?"

"We want to see you making kites," replied my friend. "We might buy one at the weekend when I get my pocket money." I knew then that Eggy was going to be my true friend; he included me in all his conversation.

Some of the balls of twine in the kite man's workshop were as big as footballs. The kites were made from grease-proof paper stretched over a thin, octagonal bamboo frame and decorated with colourful stickers. Each sticker was in actual fact a strengthener. A tiny hole in the star-shaped strengthener allowed the string through from the bamboo frame. The eight strings met and were tied together about twelve inches from the skin of the kite. Some of the frame strings were of different length. The secret, explained the strange old-fashioned man, was to tie the strings in such a way as to get the correct angle for the airflow. When we left the quaint old shop I was a kite-flying enthusiast and intended to fly a kite so high that it could not be seen by the naked eye . . .

So ended my first day in the big boys' section of St Jude's. It had been pretty good. I had a new friend, a new hobby and was a member of the football team. And being a member of the swimming team thrilled me! I had a pass to the swimming pool! Showers every day! I could keep clean for the rest of my life and it felt like being born again!

The months passed quickly. The public library beckoned. Eggy joined the library with me and the first books I took away were "Grimm's Fairy Tales" and "Robin Hood".

Spring came and the blossoms fell from the trees in Shiel Park. The hard stony ground turned to rich green grass and I joined the school cricket team with my friend. We went down in the history books as the only team to score a century and clean bowl the opposition for a duck! Cowboy Donaghue said in his gorgeous, Anglo-Welsh-Liverpool-Manx-Irish accent, "We wundem eezy! Darrell be in dee *Echo* ternite!"

"Worrell be in dee *Echo*?" asked Stanley Marsden, the back stop.

"A hundred fuckin' nil!" replied Cowboy. "Dale gerrit in da buke a fuckin' records!"

Fortunately, during my early years with Tommy Lawless, I'd been impressed by his nicely formed words and easy manner of speech. His grandmother had insisted that we read poetry aloud and she had helped me with my diction. I was only a poor, ragged kid but I did not intend to remain one all my life. True, I could eff and blind with the best of them but I tried my very best not to speak like a "buck".

The difference between a buck and an everyday scouse is this: The buck is aggressive. He says, "Warra yew luken at?" The scouse replies, "I dunno, the label's fell off." The buck threatens to hit you with a brick; the scouse says, "Gowome, yermum's got cake!"

A stranger, on asking a buck a simple question like "Where's the urinal?" would be given a surly look and the words, "Fuck off, wack!" The scouse would reply to the same question, "How many funnels has she got?" Verbal badinage comes natural to the scouse but one gets only abuse from the buck.

Eggy spoke nicely and he was always friendly and witty. If it had not been for the lunch he shared with me every day, and the empty bottles that I got from Teddy Kirkwood, then I would not have survived. Teddy and Joey Kirkwood stole hundreds of bottles of pop from the mineral water lorries but wouldn't return the empties and claim the penny deposit. I felt no guilt when I returned them. I bought fish and chips with the money and that's what kept me alive.

"'Ow's yer father . . . all right! Sitting in the ale-house . . .all night! 'Ow's yer mother . . . okay! Standing at the pawnshop . . . all day!" That's a little snatch from a skipping rope song.

Someone, some body or organisation, actually cared about the poorest of us; we could get free dinners and free milk at school. This meant a trip to some place called the "dinner house" and the carrying of a pink ticket in order to claim the right to such things.

There were times when I was sorely tempted to apply for a pink ticket but some kind of inner pride prevented me. There were only three or four kids in the whole school who went to the dinner house. Five minutes before lunch break, the teacher would call out: "Those of you who are going to the dinner house can get away now!" Not a single lad in my class moved and I don't think any one of us even knew where the dinner house was situated.

CHAPTER THREE

A Day at the Races

Joey Kirkwood wanted me to go to the Grand National with him. His brother, who usually accompanied him on all his adventures, was locked up in the local gaol for stealing a wedding cake. I felt quite guilty about this actually, because I'd helped them eat the wedding cake at the back of Charlie Redmayne's garage.

"I'm not going stealing with you," I informed the cheeky young thief.

"Who asked you?" replied Joey. "I just wanna day out at the National. I go every year. Come with me and you'll have a good time."

Joey was a wonderful kid. I liked him, but he was liable to steal anything and it scared me. The thought of seeing the greatest horse race in the world was very tempting, however. "Okay," I said. "I'll come with you but I don't want any trouble. I won't steal anything, no matter what you say."

"We're going into the grandstand with all the toffs," said Joey, "so you'll have to have some shoes on your feet."

"I ain't got any fuckin' shoes," I told him.

"Well, you can have mine," said Joey. He pulled off his shoes and stockings. "Put them on," he said. "I'm going to get some new ones." He walked into Woolworth's, picked out a nice pair of stockings, stuffed them up his jersey and walked out of the door.

"Timpson's next stop," he said when we got round the corner. "You'd better wait on the other side of the road. If you see me running like hell, don't come after me. I'll meet you at the Aintree tram stop in about ten minutes." He gave me his new stockings and walked barefoot into Timpson's shoe store.

I couldn't stand the strain so, after hanging around on the opposite side of the road for about five minutes, I walked

34

across and peeped through the shoe-shop window. Joey was sitting on a little footstool and a nice young lady was kneeling down and fastening the laces of a pair of lovely white running shoes to Joey's feet. A little kid was standing on the edge of the pavement having a pee in the gutter, his mother holding his hand as the busy shoppers passed to and fro. I took my eyes from the window for a second and my friend went past me like a streak of lightning. The shop assistant came running out of the door shouting her head off, and the kid in the gutter turned around and pee'd all over her.

It looked like being an interesting day. Aintree Racecourse was about seven miles away. I had no money for the tram and I was sure Joey didn't have enough for the pair of us. He was at the tram stop waiting for me. "What do you think of my new plimsolls?" he asked when I showed up.

"Lovely!" I replied. "Here's your socks. Will you stop pinching things, or we'll finish up in gaol!"

He sat down on the slatted tram-stop bench and put his new stockings on. "We'll have to walk for a couple of stops," he said as he tied the laces to his new footwear. "If we get on here, we'll have to pay." It was like having a day out with a whirlwind.

We skipped aboard a tramcar as it sped along Walton Road and sat upstairs. "Two tickets to the Pier Head," asked my smiling young friend, offering two pennies to the conductor.

"This car's going to Aintree Racecourse," replied the uniformed man. "You'll have to get off at the next stop, cross to the other side of the road and catch a tram that's going in the other direction."

"Thank you sir," answered Joey. He put the two coppers back in his pocket. The conductor rang the bell, the tram stopped and we got off. The conductor then went upstairs again.

"Come on," shouted Joey. "We can make another couple of stops before he gets down again. The car's full and he'll be kept busy." Two more journeys, going through the same routine and with the precious two pence still in our possession, found us safely at Aintree and only a few yards from the race track.

There were thousands of people coming from all directions, some in gleaming Rolls-Royce cars, some in simple traps pulled by beautiful tail-swishing ponies, and others on foot, cycles, motorbikes with sidecars and great fat charabancs crowded with beer-swilling race-goers.

"Are you hungry?" asked my crafty friend.

"I'm always hungry," I replied. "I could eat a horse between two bread vans!"

"What do you fancy?" asked Joey, flashing the two pence.

"I'll have the same as you," I said, licking my lips.

Joey gave me the two pennies. "Here's a good chip shop," he pointed out. "You get well behind me in the queue. If anybody runs after me, drop the money, bend down to pick it up and trip the fucker on his arse. Don't spend the two pence whatever you do. That's all we've got for our day out." A hungry belly has no conscience. I'd stolen apples from the fruit stands but nothing as sophisticated as this.

Joey reached the counter. I heard his piping voice, "Pie, chips and peas, twice!" he shouted. "Plenty of salt and vinegar please, and wrap them up well. I've a long way to go."

The nice friendly man in the white overalls and spotless apron smiled down at the sweet young angel-faced boy, but the moment that he passed the newspaper-wrapped package to young Joey, I started to shake all over. Joey fairly flew out of the shop. The man shouted, "Hey you!" and all the customers looked around, but Joey was miles away.

"I think it's going to be our lucky day," remarked my optimistic young friend, stuffing the last of the crisp, golden chips down his gob. "We'll get a couple of bottles of pop later on."

We were sitting on the damp green grass outside the turnstiles. I was in the hands of an expert and knew perfectly well that he was right. It looked like it was going to be the best day ever.

Colourful-looking race-track tipsters and touts swarmed like wasps around a jam-jar. It was like a circus: cowboys dressed in leather chaps, men dressed up as jockeys and all kinds of weird characters selling their tips.

Prince Monolulu drew the greatest crowd. He was an awe-inspiring black prince from some faraway country. He was the most wonderful-looking man I had ever seen: ten foot tall, graceful, smiling all over his handsome face with great white teeth gleaming in the noon-day sun and colourful, flowing robes billowing in the springtime breeze. His magnificent feathered head-dress fascinated me: I couldn't take my eyes off it. It was made of three-foot ostrich feathers and plumes from the bird of paradise. Ladies and gentlemen dressed in the height of fashion with diamonds glittering, gold cigarette cases flashing, strings of beautiful pearls, golden bracelets, top hats . . . they stood around and listened to his spiel. "I gotta horse! I gotta horse!" shouted Monolulu.

Flat caps and mufflers, ragged-arsed kids and jolly race-horse gamblers gathered around the prince. He swished a huge lion tail about, peeled a thick-skinned Jaffa orange and popped a segment into his laughing mouth. A tiny dribble of orange juice escaped from the corner of his handsome mouth and he captured it with a lick of his long pink tongue. People gave him money. He whispered some words of wisdom into their ear, and they went away smiling. Monolulu slashed the air with his big lion's tail, waved his handsome feathered head and shouted, "I gotta horse! I gotta horse!"

A trumpet sounded nearby. A guy dressed up in a scarlet hunting outfit gathered a crowd of rubbernecks about him. "I gave you the winner of the Lincoln!" he bawled. "You all know me! I'm not here today and gone tomorrow! I gave you Elton to win the Lincoln! And what was the price my friends? One hundred to one! Yes, ladies and gentlemen! one hundred to one!" He blew on his hunting horn and the crowd thickened.

Sun-bronzed young gypsy girls told fortunes, read your palm and jingled gorgeous earrings from their smiling faces. There were organ grinders, chattering monkeys and men with hooks instead of hands. Tumblers, acrobats and men selling toffee apples. Huge marquee tents were packed with delicious food: whole roast chickens, legs of steaming hot beef, boar's heads with oranges peeping from the open snout and silver salvers laden with poached salmon. Great magnums of champagne for the very rich and bottles of beer and cider for the not so rich.

Gentlemen in morning coats and spats scoffed oysters from the shell while working men ate cockles and mussels.

A half naked man lay on the rich green grass. He was bound hand and foot with chain and padlocks. A great big bare-chested giant of a man swung a mighty sledge-hammer around his head as if it was as light as a feather. "Step this way!" he shouted. "I am going to smash this giant boulder of granite on this poor unfortunate man's chest. Sadly, we cannot get any insurance company to cover us for this tremendous display of courage, so I am about to pass the hat among you." He hefted up a giant boulder, raised it right above his head and let it fall to the grass with a thud. A gypsy boy ran among the crowd. "Sixpence each!" he shouted. "Sixpence for today's big priced winner!" The giant swung his hammer. The boy carried on, "Only sixpence! Thank you sir! Don't tell your friends! Only a tanner for the big winner. Many thanks. Don't talk about it or the price will drop. One for you sir?"

"I wanna brave young boy!" shouted a guy in a tiger skin. "I wanna brave young boy to come forward!" He swung a gleaming shiny sabre, the wicked blade honed as sharp as a razor. He tossed an apple in the air and slashed it with a mighty swipe of the sword. A lovely young boy stepped out of the crowd and the people gasped as the tiger-skinned Hercules placed an apple on the handsome youngster's head. We waited and waited but the cunning old devil just kept us waiting while he sold his tips.

"Pull your stockings up," said Joey. "Comb your hair and make yourself look nice. We're going to get a bottle of pop and find someone to take us into the races." We straightened our stockings and combed our hair. Mounted police patrolled among the crowds and horse-boxes. There were crowds outside the turnstiles and everyone was talking about the wonderful prices because there were sixty-six runners which was an all-time record.

Joey led the way to the most expensive turnstile. "Just follow me and do whatever I do when I give you the nod," he said in his self-assured way. He studied the faces carefully. "Now!" he said and ducked under the turnstile. I was close on his heels. Joey pointed his forefinger to a nicely dressed gentleman and shouted: "There's me dad!"

A big, rough-looking attendant put his hand on young Joey's shoulder, looked across at the man in the turnstile and nodded to the gate-keeper.

"Are they with you sir?" asked the gate-keeper.

"Of course they're with me!" snapped the well-dressed gentleman. "No charge for children is there?"

We were in the grandstand! There were quite a few races and we saw everything quite clearly. It was a fantastic race track and the colourful silks of the jockeys, gorgeous sleek animals and laughing winners created such a wonderful spectacle that I thought it must be a dream. When the sixty-six horses paraded out of the paddock and made their way, skinny-bellied and wild-eyed, to the starting post, I had to pinch myself just to make sure. The crowd went wild; there was laughter and loud cheering as the famous riders flashed past and race-goers shouted to their favourite jockeys.

The starter raised his white flag, a great roar went up from the Aintree crowd and they were off! Beautiful horses went sailing through the air: over the spruce fences, rail and ditch fences they galloped madly, boots and whips and swishing tails; over the brooks and round the turn, on and on they went, over valentines, over the rails . . . "Come on, you bastard!" shouted a top-hatted gentleman near my ear. It was so exciting! Horses stumbled and fell, jockeys rolled themselves up into a tight little ball and prayed that the other horses would jump over them. "Easter Hero! Easter Hero! Come on, you cockeyed bastard!" shouted the rich gentleman. He threw his top hat down and screamed with rage but jockey Joe Moloney couldn't help poor Easter Hero. He was six lengths behind Gregalach; Gregalach won at one hundred to one and poor Easter Hero finished second in a lather of sweaty foam. Only nine of the wonderful horses finished the course. The toughest steeplechase in the world had taken its heavy toll. The other fifty-seven horses were rounded up and somehow made their way back to the stables.

The sport of kings! The sport of ragged-arsed kids and top-hatted gentlemen cursing the brave animals. . . It had been so wonderful! One man won a pile of money, stuffed it into his hat and gave us half-a-crown. We paid our fares on the tramcar home, shared the rest and promised ourselves another day at the Grand National. Unfortunately it only took place once a year, but I knew I would go again.

CHAPTER FOUR

Street Boy

Life wasn't all dirt and misery. There was the thrill of running. I was underfed and underweight but I could run like hell! Racing back to school from the rocks at Shaw Street Park with the one o'clock gun as the starter. Racing from St Francis Xavier to the top of Prescot Street with Nobbler Almond in five minutes flat. Racing the tramcars from Grant's Gardens to the Everton picture palace. Jumping from rooftop to rooftop in the black of night with the skill of a cat. Swimming, football and jumping on fast moving lorries for a free ride.

But my greatest thrill was the cinema . . . I lived in the cinema!

One of my mates asked me to go to the pictures with him.

"What's it like?" I asked, tossing a ha'penny piece on my thumb and forefinger and catching the spinning copper coin in my dirty palm like an expert.

"It's fuckin' smashin'! Haven't you ever been to the fuckin' pictures?"

"Course not. It costs fuckin' money to go to the pictures. I'd sooner play climbing on the back jigger walls."

"It don't cost much, you cunt. Not in the 'Lousy Lytton' anyway."

"How much does it cost?" I enquired, spinning my ha'penny about six feet high.

"A penny! A fuckin' penny, that's all!"

"I've only got a ha'penny," I admitted.

"Okay. I'll toss you for the fuckin' ha'penny. If you win you come to the Lytton with me, and if I win I can buy two fuckin' oranges from the Mary Ellens."

"How much have you got?" I asked.

"Three ha'pence," he said proudly. "One and a half fuckin' dee."

"Okay. You call. Heads or tails?"

"Heads," shouted my mate.

Up went the spinning copper coin.

"Tails!" I claimed, putting my dirty foot on the precious coin in case it went down the drain.

"You win, Jackie. Will you come with me now? Take the fuckin' ha'penny!"

"Okay. Let's frig off!"

Hundreds of dirty looking, ragged-arsed kids lined the pavement. Some of the girls wore shoes, but all the boys were barefoot and most had holes in their trousers from which peeped a couple of inches of dirty hide.

"Tuppenny customers walk right in!" shouted the doorman. "Plenny a room in the tupp'ny's!"

"What's it like in the tuppenny seats?" I enquired.

"Fuckin' useless!" replied my mate. "You have to stand up if some big-headed cunt gets in front of you. The penny seats are best. If we're quick off the mark we can get on the front row."

"Peanuts!" shouted the Mary Ellen.

"Save my place," whispered my mate. "I'm going to knock some peanuts off."

"Peanuts! Penny a pound peanuts!"

The kids shuffled about, and the queue got longer and longer until it almost filled the long narrow street from end to end.

"Tangerines! Big juicy Jaffa oranges!"

My mate came back with a school cap full of peanuts in his hands. "Shove this lot down your shirt," he said. "I'm going back for a couple of tangerines."

"Where did you get the cap?"

"I pinched it off some silly cunt's head. Where do you think I got it? Offa fuckin' tree?!"

"Any more for the tuppennys?" shouted the doorman. "Right! Have your money ready, you lot, and keep quiet when you get inside."

It felt strange and exciting. The lady at the cash desk gave me a metal disk with a hole in it in exchange for my penny and the man on the inner door took my disk, threaded it onto a great steel needle and watched it take a journey down a long hanging cord.

"Hurry up, Jackie! Get a front seat!" It was so exciting! All the scruffy kids were laughing and shouting, breaking peanut shells, tearing the skins from juicy oranges and throwing them at each other, at the screen, on the floor and all over the place.

A beautiful young lady, all blonde and smelling of tart's perfume, came onto the stage right in front of me.

"Who's the judy?" I asked my mate.

"That's the pianist," he said. "Shut up! A big guy hits you on the head with a friggin' great long cane if you make a noise after she sits down."

She arranged some sheets of music on the piano stand, and sat down . . .

"KEEP QUIET!!!" shouted a tall grey-haired man.

"Sh!" whispered my mate. "That's the guy."

"Keep quiet!" A seven or eight foot long cane, almost like a fishing rod, lashed across the row of seated ragamuffins and landed on somebody's shoulder. "I won't tell you again!" shouted Mr Ariel Gray, the proprietor.

An old guy in a tatty-looking uniform walked down one side of the cinema and turned the gas lights low. An old woman walked up the other side doing the same thing, and then the piano started up.

It was thrilling! My first visit to a cinema . . . I was spellbound! The films were silent and the words came up on the screen. Some of the kids could not read very well, so they kept up a little conversation with a companion: "What did she say? Read it aloud! Fuckin' 'ell!!! He's going to shoot! Look out!"

"Keep quiet!!!" shouted Ariel Gray.

"Do you like the peanuts, Jackie?"

"Yes," I whispered. "What's all that water under our feet?"

"Piss! The bucks from Scotland Road always piss on the floor."

Suddenly . . . a train came straight at me. I shouted "Look Out!!!" and went to my knees on the piss-wet floor.

I was a movie addict from that day on. I think I must have seen every movie that was ever made, and spent most of my life in the twenty or more cinemas in and around the great seaport where I lived.

My favourite cinema was the Olympia, a magnificent,

splendid, imposing and brightly-lit house of entertainment. It had six balustraded balconies, starting from the plush red velvet of the dress circle with its gorgeous pit orchestra, and going higher and higher. The higher you went, the cheaper the seats became, until eventually you were sitting up in the Gods on wood-covered stone slabs, and staring down at a silver screen no bigger than a postage stamp. The climb, however, was quite an ordeal and many's the time I've seen people sitting on the cold concrete steps, only halfway to the "Gods", puffing and panting and trying to get their breath back, legs turned to jelly.

There was a brightly polished brass handrail on either side of the stairway to the stars but the only people who seemed to use the handrails were one-legged guys. Liverpool crawled with one-legged guys, or maybe it hopped . . . The missing legs had been left in a place called France, and this puzzled me as a child: "Oh! I left one leg in France . . . And the other didn't stand a chance! . . . You left me like a broken doll!" That's what my dad's mate used to sing when they got drunk together and Billy gave his speciality: a one-legged dance routine. Billy was funny and he really could dance.

Anyway, as they got drunk every day of the week, slept it off in the parlour and then went out again in the evening for a session that would last until chucking-out time, Billy got plenty of practice. He was an expert at getting drunk, but not as expert as my Dad. He was the best! Dad's special boast was: "So I hit the friggin' horse with my fist and knocked it stone cold with one punch . . ." He had too . . . He had fists like slabs of concrete, was one of Liverpool's hard men and it took six policemen to lock him up, which was two or three times a month when he went "bobby beating", his other favourite hobby.

It was cold sitting on the flat bench seats up in the Gods, but it didn't bother me all that much because I hadn't paid to get in, and this particular day the man sitting next to me had just slipped his big warm overcoat across my bare legs. Without giving him a second glance, I settled down to watch the movie and enjoy the antics of my favourite actor, Johnny Weissmuller: Tarzan of the Apes.

Queues were the least of my worries. I had a piece of wire in my pocket and with it I could open any cinema or theatre door in the city, slip upstairs, sneak into the lavatory for a few minutes and then take a seat as if I had been a paying customer.

Unfortunately, I had to choose the cheaper seats because of my appearance. If I'd some decent clothes on my skinny frame and a pair of shoes on my dirty feet, then I wouldn't be sitting in the Gods: I'd be snuggled down in the deep red plush, listening to the delightful crackle of chocolate wrappings and sniffing the rich aroma from the fat cigars.

However, I was quite at home among the flat caps and the blue smoke that curled up into the glittering ceiling, polluted the air and caused the members of the entranced audience to cough their tubercular lungs up!

Weissmuller was in dead trouble with a savage-looking lion and it looked as if the mighty king of the jungle would finish off my hero. The movie held me in its spell, otherwise I might have noticed what the guy sitting next to me was doing, and it is just possible that I would have objected.

A warm feeling crept over me and pleasure ran over my skin like water. The man's hand rested on my leg, and the heat from it seemed to penetrate the coat, making me feel lovely and comfortable.

Strange sensations that I had never experienced before filled me with happiness, made my knees tremble and my body tingle all over. The whole of the strange man's forearm rested comfortably on my lap and a slight pressure brought my blood to the boil, made my senses reel and supplied me with the utmost pleasure and delight.

Blood ran from a gaping wound in my hero's chest and the savage lion clawed him yet again . . . Tarzan dropped his knife, slippery with his sweat and pumping life fluids. There was not much hope for the muscular Johnny Weissmuller this time. The lion let out a mighty roar, his great head opening into a sharp-fanged, cavernous and frightening aperture. Saliva dripped from it, ran over Tarzan's shoulder and trickled down his bare bronzed back.

"Look out! Look out!" I screamed, stamping my feet with excitement and almost falling over the balcony and into the sixpenny seats. Tarzan, however, let rip his ear-piercing yell, thumped his massive chest and killed the tawny king of beasts with his bare hands.

"Exciting, isn't it?" said the smiling friendly-looking man. "Do you like it?"

"Yeah!" I was not in the mood for conversation and wanted to watch the movie.

The guy tucked his coat over me and patted my leg in a friendly way. His leg moved closer and pressed quite firm against mine. "Are you warmer now son?"

"Yeah, thanks," I said, grateful for the warmth of his coat but wishing he'd shut up.

His hand fell heavily on my knee and his leather shoe pressed on my bare foot making me wince. "Sorry kid," said my companion. "Did I stand on your foot?"

"It's okay; it didn't hurt."

It was a sort of opening for him, a kind of springboard for his next move which was to raise the coat, run his hand down my bare leg and take hold of my foot. "Are you sure I didn't hurt you?" he said, smiling at me after he'd examined my foot, run his hand up my leg again and given my knee a kind of reassuring friendly squeeze.

"It's okay. Really. I'm fine."

We settled down again, but his fingers gripped my hand and held on to me beneath the coat. I thought nothing of it, and supposed he was just being friendly and apologetic.

"Are you enjoying yourself?" he whispered. His warm hand was on my leg and it felt cosy and comforting.

"Sure I like it . . . Look, there's Cheeta!" I laughed at the antics of the chattering chimpanzee, clapping my hands with glee as he clung to the apeman's broad shoulders and they swung away into the safety of the tall green trees and surrounding jungle – a jungle alive with snakes, fearsome black warriors, spotted leopards and crawling, long-tailed, awesome crocodiles.

The man's hand crept higher and my leg got warmer as his fingers crept up into my short grey trousers and rested gently on my aroused young penis. It was almost as exciting as Tarzan and I did not object as he played with me and stroked the stiffened organ to the point of no return. A tickling feeling, so sensational that it almost made me cry out with pleasure, overcame me and I could stand it no longer. My hand reached beneath the heavy overcoat and gripped my companion's moving fingers. He took my hand in a firm grasp and pushed it into his open trouser front hidden beneath the coat.

The huge, throbbing penis filled my childish hand and frightened me for a moment. Then I felt the soft warmth of pubic hair and it fascinated me to such an extent that I let go of the sexual organ and contented myself with the mysterious capillature, stroking, fondling and playing with the twisty hairs.

"Pull me off!" he whispered. "Stop playin' about and pull me off!" I must have been about ten or eleven years old at the time and I had not even pulled myself off! He gripped my fingers and placed them on the sexy pole sticking up beneath the overcoat.

"Like this!" he whispered, moving my clutching hand up and down. "Keep doing it till I tell you to stop. Jesus, you're a lovely kid! What's your name?"

"Jackie."

"Well, toss me off, Jackie, and when we get outside I'll buy you some sweets or something."

He was quite a pleasant young man and he was very excited. I could hardly believe that anyone could possess such an enormous penis, as hard as a bar of steel and as thick as my young hand could span. My own erection had not gone down as yet and I was still unable to produce the magic fluid that my mates called "spunk". This guy must have had quite a lot, however, for it suddenly shot from him, splashed onto his belly, up into the folds of the coat and over my knuckles. I was amazed, scared and somewhat ashamed of myself as I fastened my trousers and carried on watching the movie.

"Jackie!" the guy whispered in my ear. "You wouldn't talk about this to anyone, would you?"

"No." I wouldn't have dared!

"You're a nice kid! Are you going to stay in and see the film again?"

"Yes. I always see the films twice over. There's nothing else to do."

When the lights went up and the girl came round with her tray, my friendly companion bought me an ice cream and put his arm around my shoulder as if I were his young son. He bought some popcorn, lit a cigarette and talked away as if it was the most natural thing in the world. I began to like him, and his friendly manner disarmed me and put me at ease. It must have been almost ten thirty when we eventually left the cinema. Once outside, he took me into the dark alleyway at the rear and stood me in the shadows of the huge building.

"You're a smashing kid," he said, opening his trousers and showing me the enormous thing I had been playing with. "Do it again!" Before I could make up my mind whether to run away in fear or play with the throbbing organ, he opened my trousers and took my dickie in his mouth. I was astonished! He sucked it as if it was a lollipop and he obviously enjoyed it. It went on for quite some time and while I was too scared to run away, in fact I think I enjoyed it too. When the unbelievable tickling sensation overcame me and I withdrew my stiff wet dickie, giggling and wriggling and writhing with unexpected pleasure and excitement, the man kissed me.

He pulled away at his long penis. "Watch it shoot out," he said, pulling faster and faster. "Watch it shoot . . .! Wow!" Creamy white, sticky-looking globules shot from the monstrous penis like silver bullets from the Lone Ranger's pistol and splashed against the dark red exit doors of the Olympia cinema.

Flipping his penis back into his trousers, the man took me by the hand. "Come along, Jackie. I'll put you on the tram and see you get home safe. How old are you, by the way?"

"Eleven."

"Does no one look after you?"

"What do you mean?"

"A kid like you shouldn't be running around barefoot. Doesn't your mother look after you? You haven't even got a decent jersey on your back and I don't suppose you ever had a coat in your life."

Most of the kids in my little world ran barefoot and not many of them had coats so it didn't bother me – I just shrugged my thin shoulders and laughed. The guy took me home on the tramcar, kissed my forehead in the shadow of the back entrance to my filthy house and asked me to meet him again.

"Would you like to see me on Saturday?" he said. "I'll take you home with me and see if I can dig out some shoes and stockings for you, then I'll take you to the zoo or some place."

I had got used to him by this time and he seemed concerned about me so I nodded my head. "Yes, I'd like to go to the zoo."

"Okay, Jackie. Meet me outside the Royal Hippodrome about ten o'clock Saturday morning." He turned as if to go, then took me in his arms and kissed my forehead again. "Please don't say anything to anybody. Not a word. Not even to your best friend. Okay?"

I didn't even know his name, where he lived or anything about him, and I had no intention of meeting him again. He rumpled my hair in a friendly sort of way and vanished into the darkness of the back jigger.

My mother was waiting for me when I opened the door and gave me a belt over the ear with a wet, smelly hand. "Where have you been? You dirty, friggin' gett!"

My father usually called me a scruffy-looking bastard and, if he was sober enough to catch me, endorsed the words with a stinging slap from his belt. He was out of condition this time and also out of luck. "Bastard!" he shouted, chasing me around the big white kitchen table. "Bastard! Wait till I get my friggin' hands on you!"

Unfortunately, my elder sister got in my way and I had to dive under the table, but I managed to escape and went upstairs to bed. We had gas lighting in my home but I had to go to bed in the dark. It bothered me at times because I liked to read before I slept, and I had a great collection of comics, my only possessions. Eggy, my school friend, had lent me his torch, so I could switch it on and read my comics beneath the twill, flea-speckled sheets that separated my shirt-tailed body from the rough, damp overcoats. Later, when all was quiet, and providing I had not fallen asleep, I would sneak downstairs on the freezing cold lino, search the kitchen cupboards and hope to find a piece of bread and perhaps a scrape of margarine. The wind usually blew through the kitchen door during these forays, lifting up my shirt tail, freezing my bottom and making me shiver. The stone floor in the kitchen didn't bother me at all, because my feet were tough and calloused: hardened, horny and unfeeling.

That night, however, sleep evaded me. All I could think about was the strange man who had befriended me, and the shameful feeling, excited by a consciousness of guilt, kept me awake until the early hours. The disgraceful exposure in the darkness and my own indecent behaviour worried me, and I thought perhaps I was indeed "a dirty friggin' gett" . . .

No morning sunshine shed its glory through the rich green trees and no birds sang when I awoke, dragged my ragged grey shorts on and ran to school unwashed and barefoot.

There were no trees, and the streets were thick with fog and lined with horse manure. Fog horns blared on the Mersey as huge cart-horses pulled their heavy loads along the miserable roads, slipping on the square stone sets, dropping a few more loads of steaming manure and adding streaming yellow stinking urine to the mess for other cart-horses to trample in and slither on.

Nevertheless, I enjoyed my morning journey to school: St Jude's Church of England. Good old St Jude! The patron saint of lost causes . . .

Bottles of milk stood cold and lonely on the doorsteps of the wealthy. I had never tasted real milk in my life and I liked the condensed milk which always graced our table. Its colourful tin and jagged-edged lid were the only things worth looking at, as the table was usually piled with dirty plates and dirtier-looking cups and saucers. But always amidst the jumble of unwashed crockery stood a dish of brown-stained lumpy sugar, a cracked saucer of margarine and the good old tin of "conny onny". I could grab a slice of bread, dip one of the dirty table knives into the tin and spread the sticky, sweet mess on the stolen staff of life which was my breakfast.

It was one of those days when everything was going to be just fine and dandy and you knew it instinctively. Joey Kirkwood had pinched a big bunch of bananas from the greengrocer shop and couldn't eat the whole lot by himself, so he gave me two and I wolfed them down. Eggy invited me to his home and promised me a load of comics. And it was swimming bath day: a chance to get clean and have a good time into the bargain. Swimming and running – how I loved those two sports!

We lined up outside the school and the deputy headmaster said: "Right! Lead on you lot, and don't pinch anything from the fruit stands on the way or you'll all finish up in the Bridewell." Nobbler, one of the smart-arsed kids, had a special overcoat with no lining in the pockets and a draw-string bag tied around his waist which his mother used when she was out shoplifting. As we passed the fruit stands, his long flapping overcoat brushed against the luscious-looking goodies and his unseen hands grabbed and filled the "knock off" pouch with apples, oranges and plums. We reached the swimming baths at Margaret Street loaded with fruit and one or two bottles of pop for good measure. He was quite a specialist at that sort of thing and he was generous to his hungry mates.

None of us had towels and only one boy had a pair of swimming trunks. He had reached the pubescent stage in life; thick red hair sprouted from his pubic region and the headmaster had bought him a pair of trunks to spare the lad's blushes. The rest of us swam naked and, as the sexes did not meet in the swimming baths in those days, this was the norm. The corporation supplied us with hard, rough towels and we shared two to a cubicle when we changed.

Eggy and I dried our skinny bodies in the privacy of the cubicle, and for the first time in my life I felt slightly embarrassed with my friend. My dicky stiffened up and Eggy laughed. "You've got a hard on, Jackie."

"I can't help that," I said blushing. "You get one sometimes, I suppose."

He pulled back his pointed-looking foreskin and a small red end appeared. His pigeon got hard and stiff and he played with it in front of me. "Let me do it for you," he said excitedly, "and you do it for me." I had seen other lads do it together so I agreed and we pulled our stupid organs until the sensations overcame us and we had to stop. Neither one of us could produce the mysterious fluid but we certainly tried hard enough. I was tempted to tell him about my adventure with the stranger in the cinema but thought better of it. I knew he would not believe me if I told him the guy had sucked the damn thing like a gobstopper.

Eggy was a nice respectable boy from a good clean home. Unfortunately he had no father, but his mother adored him and she rather liked me for some reason or other. When we reached his house, he invited me in. His friendly mother kissed him and rumpled my hair, laughing. "My goodness, you do smell nice and clean. What have you been up to?" I blushed like a schoolgirl, thinking about the things we had been up to and going a bright red.

"We've been swimming," said her son, laughing and tossing his black curls. "Can Jackie stay to tea with us?"

"Certainly, darling. Go and play and I'll call you when it's ready." We ran up to his room and he pulled out a pile of comics. They were all my favourites and I wanted to devour every one of them, so I sat cross-legged on the warm, carpeted floor and opened up a *Hotspur*.

Eggy ran his hand up my shorts and felt me. "You can read them any time," he said, taking my penis between his fingers and making it stiff. "Put them away and let's play dicks."

We were not exactly mealy-mouthed kids and we came from a rough neighbourhood, but swearing in your friend's house was taboo, almost as bad as smoking in front of your parents or swearing in front of a girl. But sometimes it just came out and this was one of those times. "Fuck off! Fuck off, Eggy, and leave my cock alone. What's up with you anyway?"

He simply smiled at me and said, "Sorry. I thought you liked pulling off! Don't fall out with me!"

"Okay, Eggy. I don't want to fall out with you. You know I don't. Let's read the comics; your mother will be calling us down for tea in a minute."

He piled up his comics and arranged them in alphabetical order. Then he turned to me and smiled, saying, "You can take this lot home with you when you go. I've read all of them and they're no use to me." It was very generous of him because he could swap them for others he had not read and it would save him quite a lot of pocket money.

"How would you like to spend the weekend with me?" he asked. "Mom won't mind and we can play with my Meccano set."

It seemed like a good idea and I wanted to stay in his comfortable home because I didn't have much, and the thought of eating his mother's home-made cakes made my mouth water. However, I had not stayed with anyone before and was not quite sure what my mother would say, apart from "Dirty, friggin' gett".

"Jesus, Eggy! I'd love to spend a weekend with you. Are you sure your mother won't mind?"

"Of course she won't," he laughed. "She likes you and she thinks you're one of the best kids around here." We fooled about laughing and joking until his mother called us downstairs and the three of us sat at the table. It was spotless! The food was delightful and his friendly mother smelled of home-made cake and crushed violets. I think I fell in love with her, and wished I had someone like her to give me a few kisses and a smile like the ones she continually showered upon her handsome young son.

She invited me to spend Saturday night and all day Sunday, and when I reached home laden down with comics I thought it must be Christmas.

Strangely enough my mother did not object and I waited out the rest of the week patiently. Thinking about Eggy and his continual sexy advances kept me awake at night, and when Saturday morning came round I was standing outside the Royal Hippodrome at ten o'clock wondering if the strange man would keep his promise and take me to the zoo.

He showed up dead on time, took me by the hand and jumped onto a waiting bus holding me tight. I hardly recognised him in the daylight and he looked so expensively dressed and well groomed that I felt shabby and ashamed. The man paid the fares and whispered quietly, "I'm glad you showed up, Jackie. Are you sure you didn't tell anyone about what happened? I'm sorry about the whole thing and I want to take you home and look after you. I won't bother you, honestly."

He seemed so kind and friendly. I knew he must be the only one besides Eggy's mother who cared about me. He squeezed my hand affectionately and ran his gentle fingers through my hair. "This is where we get off", he said in a nice quiet voice. "You're not scared, are you?"

"What of?" I asked. "What is there to be scared of?"

"Good!" he replied, holding me by the hand. "A couple of blocks down the road and we are home." I clung on to his big strong hand and tried to match his stride, skipping as I went.

"I have some clothes that should fit you," he said. "I've got some nice shoes also, but I had to make a guess at the size. If they don't fit you, the man in the shop will change them."

The house was lovely: green front lawn, garage, a beautiful garden at the rear, tall pointed trees, bushy-looking laurels and colourful beds of flowers. He turned the key in the front door and a few seconds later sat me on a nice comfy settee. I felt a little shy and out of place. He patted my head gently and said: "Take it easy, son."

Then he went into the kitchen and returned carrying a glass of milk in one hand and a plate of sandwiches in the other. "Get that down you," he said, switching on the radio, lighting a cigarette and acting rather nervous.

They didn't even have a radio in Eggy's house, and although I had often heard them blasting from the open shop doorways, I'd never seen one in a person's home. It fascinated me. The sandwiches were delicious and the glass of fresh milk absolutely out of this world!

"I hope you're going to forgive me for what happened the other night," he said, unbuttoning my shirt. "I don't know what came over me and I'm very sorry." He slipped my shirt off and ran an expert hand over my chest, shoulders and upper arms.

"You're a fine big lad," he said, "but you could do with putting some weight on. Come and see me as often as you can and I'll feed you up, fill you out and make you strong and healthy."

Lots of kids in my school were skinny and under-nourished. I thought I was fit and husky compared with them.

"Let's have your trousers off, Jackie." Having complete confidence in the friendly man and believing sincererly that he meant me no harm, I stood up and let my tatty grey shorts drop to the floor.

He took me by the hand and led me naked to the bathroom. It was beautiful. A stack of soft fresh towels, pink and blue tablets of perfumed toilet soap and a fluffy looking yellow sponge caught my eye. Real toilet tissue, colourful and hygienic, hung from a modern chromium-plated dispenser and a pink and white bath tub was almost full with fragrant bubbly water, blue with bath crystals and a sheer delight to my nostrils. Chintzy little curtains blew gently in the light breeze from the open window and even the floor was carpeted. Everything was so very fresh and clean that it almost took my breath away!

The man picked me up in his strong brown arms and deposited me gently in the tub. "Enjoy yourself, Jackie. I'm going to get your new clothes. Then I'll shampoo your hair and make you smell nice. Would you like that?"

I threw him one of my best smiles, took my nose between finger and thumb and slid beneath the warm and bubbly fresh water. It was utter bliss!

"What's your name?" I asked when he returned with a neat stack of clothes and a new toothbrush in a cellophane wrapper.

"Eddie. Just call me Eddie. I'm a policeman. Does that surprise you?" Eddie squirted some sweet-smelling shampoo into my hair and rubbed it into a gorgeous foamy lather. Bubbles ran down my face, onto my lips and streamed thick and foamy on my chest. He made me stand up in the lovely pink bathtub and washed me as carefully and as gently as a loving parent. He even examined my feet, made me open my mouth and inspected my teeth.

"Open your mouth and clean your teeth like this," he said, showing me the up and down motion and squeezing some minty-flavoured paste on the brush. "You are lucky. All your teeth are perfect and you must keep them like that all your life! This brush is for you and I want you to use it every day."

It was lovely and I wanted it to last forever, but eventually he picked me out of the warm tub and stood me on the bathroom rug.

"Did you enjoy that?"

"Fabulous! It's the first time I've had a bath."

"Well, how do you keep clean?"

"The swimming pool. They have a foot bath and a shower. But we don't have a bath at home."

He rubbed my face dry with a sweet-smelling towel and kissed me on the lips as light as a feather.

"Do you mind me kissing you, Jackie? I mean no harm."

"Not really. I've never been kissed."

"Doesn't your father kiss you?"

"No. But he belts me with a piece of horse harness."

"How about your mother? She must have kissed you. . ."

"She stinks! I mean she really smells! And I wouldn't let her kiss me, even if she tried."

He rubbed me down with the thick fragrant towel and wrapped a smaller one around my head like a turban.

"You look lovely," he whispered. "Do you mind if I kiss you again?"

"No. I don't mind. . . I think I like it. . . But I can't imagine you being a policeman."

"Well, I am, and I'll be kissing you all day long if we don't get you dressed."

Eddie slipped a snow-white open-necked cricket shirt over me and put me into a pair of boy's knickers. It was the first time I had worn undershorts and it felt strange. A bright V-necked sweater and a pair of modern, well-cut shorts came next. Then he brushed my mop of curly black hair and stroked it lovingly.

"God forgive me! I can hardly keep my hands off you!" He kissed me lightly on the lips and helped me into a thick pair of knee-length woollen stockings. They were white and looked marvellous. A pair of polished leather brogues came next and they fitted perfectly.

"What do you think?" asked Eddie. The mirror was all steamed up and I couldn't really see myself, but I felt like a toff! Eddie took my hand and led me into the bedroom where a huge mirrored wardrobe stood, and I looked at myself in my new outfit. I could hardly believe my own eyes.

"What's the matter?" he asked quietly when the tears began to fall. "I don't know, Eddie. . . I'm wondering what my mother will do. She'll probably pawn everything on Monday morning and all your good kind deeds will be for nothing. I'll be back where I started and it's all so hopeless."

Eddie took me in his arms. "Please don't cry, son." He kissed my hair. "I'll keep an eye on you. I wish you were my son."

"I wish you were my dad, Eddie."

"So do I! So do I! I'm afraid I'm going to kiss you every time I see you. I just can't help it."

I had to stroke his face and whisper, "I don't mind! I really don't mind, Eddie."

"Come on!" he said. "There's a circus at Newsham Park – lions, tigers and elephants. We can have your photograph taken and I'll be able to look at it even after you have grown up."

It was good having my photo taken. We had three copies and I kept looking at the one in my pocket and thinking how smart I looked.

I'm not sure what happened in the thirties in other big cities, but in Liverpool the police had a special fund for clothing poor children. It was the normal thing if a policeman recommended it, for him to use his discretion, draw on the fund and help with the poorer families. Unfortunately, the miserable families were so very poor that the kid's clothing got pawned for a few shillings and that was the end of it. So the police opened up another scheme called "Police Clothing". These garments were all made of brown corduroy and the pawnshops were not allowed to take them in. It was a very good idea but it backfired! The brown cords branded a kid as a poverty-stricken "gett" and the kids refused to wear them.

When the circus ended and Eddie took me to his home again, I said, "What do I tell my mother? How do I explain the new clothes?"

"Tell her to get in touch with the police station," he said. "Everything is all fixed up. Compliments of the Goodfellows organisation." Later on he kissed me goodbye and I went round to Eggy's house to spend the night with him. A key to Eddie's lovely home almost burned a hole in my pocket and made my heart beat faster. . . Somebody cared!

My mother seemed quite pleased with my good fortune and the packages I returned home with. "We might get a Goodfellows parcel every month," she said, "and we're bound to get one at Christmas, now that we're on their list."

However, I still went to school barefoot, dressed in my tatty grey shorts and ragged jersey. But when evening came, I washed carefully, put my nice outfit on and called on my new friend looking spotless, my hair well groomed and my teeth sparkling.

There were times when I sat upon his knee and there were times when he kneeled before me. Most certainly we indulged in mild sexual play, but nothing against my wishes and nothing unsavoury. The things we did together were always friendly, affectionate and mutually satisfying. Many warm kisses passed our lips. Tender words were spoken and we became very close.

Sometimes I would let myself into his home and he would be on duty in the city streets, so I made myself a cup of tea and waited for him. If he happened to be going on night duty, I would find him asleep, make him a cup of tea and awaken him with a smile, a kiss and a few little cuddles. We played chess together and he taught me how to box. A city cop in Liverpool most certainly had to know how to defend himself and Eddie could take on the toughest thugs, knock their silly heads together and drag them to gaol single-handed.

Life took on a new meaning for me and it was absolutely great! But one day my mother folded all my things together and put them in a cardboard box.

"You can only wear them on Sundays," she said, admiring my polished brown shoes. "Let me have the shoes as well; you'll only ruin them and I can get you an old pair of plimsolls to play about in." I had thought about wearing the outfit "for best", as the saying goes, and it seemed like a good idea at the time, but when I decided to call upon Eddie the following Sunday, the outfit was nowhere to be found. I had brushed my teeth until they sparkled. My hair was washed and carefully groomed. Even my feet were washed and clean.

"Where are my new clothes, ma?"

"In the friggin' pawnshop! Bugger off!"

I buggered off! Tears streamed down my cheeks and I never forgot the incident for the remainder of my days. I despised her from then on.

For years afterwards I would look at the picture of myself, thinking how smart I could look, and admiring the lovely sweater and snow-white cricket shirt. I was too ashamed to visit Eddie again, and for the next few months got deeply involved with Eggy. We still had not reached the stage in life when we could produce semen but we played until a tickling sensation, so wonderfully exciting, overpowered us and we had to stop.

The comic books we shared and swapped, the visits to the park, the swimming and running together – all took on a very minor role in our young lives. The only important thing now was the secret love that developed between us. I remember coming home from the public library with him, going to his house and finding a note from his mother. "Mam's gone to the pictures and she won't be back till late," he announced. "She says here: 'Make some tea for you and your friend, and get something to eat from the chip shop for both of you.' " Obviously we were very happy at the prospect of being alone but we had not planned it.

Their home had a new radio by this time and we sat together listening to the music. At six o'clock we went to the chip shop, bought our tea and ate it in the comfort of his home, discussing a match between Everton and Liverpool. Our headmaster Pat Kelly, who was chairman of Liverpool Boys', had given us free tickets and we were very interested as we were good footballers and played for the school team.

"Come up to my room, " said my friend. "I've got a scrap book with all the players' pictures in."

Perhaps it was the intimacy of his room, sitting together on his bed, or simply strong physical attraction. Whatever it was, it united us, brought us together in a new way. We jumped into bed naked. I had a few pubic hairs by this time and was past twelve years of age. We searched in vain for hairs on my lovely friend, but he seemed happy enough stroking mine.

We must have played "dicks" a hundred times but neither of us had ejaculated as yet. This time however, we tried something else. I am not quite sure who started it first, but it worked! It was the most exciting night of my life. Unfortunately, I did not see the magic fluid because it vanished into the young body of my gentle schoolfriend. He was equally successful and we became much closer.

Every morning on our way to school, my friend bought sweets, crisps, comic books and all the things that schoolboys buy. He shared everything with me because I never had any money during the week. At weekends Eggy had no cash, but I had money from a small part-time job and I shared it, paid for visits to the cinema, football matches and days out in the park.

We planned our love-making intelligently. . . we had to, because we liked to undress. It wasn't too difficult; the nights when his mum went to the cinema left us with the opportunity to lie naked on his single bed. We no longer played with our fat little pigeons or searched for growing pubic hair; we simply cuddled, held each other warm and close, kissed, watched the magic wands grow hard with desire and moved our warm young bellies together until we were slippery with clear fluid. Strangely enough, we knew it was quite natural for us and had no feelings of shame or guilt when we entered into our secret cave, filled it with little pearls of love and wonderful satisfaction.

Then we would lie side by side, looking into one another's eyes, kissing tiny boyish nipples, lips, eyelids and small freckled noses. Words of love never passed our lips and I don't think we spoke about our feelings, but we were in love and knew it well.

We made sure of well-timed little jobs like baby-sitting by volunteering and never accepting any payment, usually for his married sister and her young husband who enjoyed the temporary release from a couple of very young children who always slept soundly enough. This was our house of utmost pleasure, because they had a car, went out for the whole evening, and could be heard returning noisily. Here we indulged in the most beautiful love-making of all: looking into each other's eyes as one of us entered the magic circle.

The first time it happened was quite an experiment. "Let me try it like this," said Eggy. "Lie down on your back, lift up your legs and show me your bottom. It'll be like a boy and girl."

It was tender and delightful; Eggy stroked my smooth cheek with the back of his nice clean fingers, kissed my belly once or twice and then entered me quite easily. It made me feel like a young girl being seduced. Seeing his handsome smiling face above me gave me almost as much pleasure as the firm young penis in my bottom. My lovely friend had always been the driving force and seemed more masculine than me. He moved a little faster and a lock of soft dark curls fell upon his forehead. His lips parted and I saw his pink tongue and gleaming teeth. His eyes opened very wide and he stopped moving. I knew it was going to happen immediately. My dickie throbbed, stiffened just a little harder, quivered springy on my belly and fluid shot from it like silver pearls, landing on my chest.

"Did you enjoy it like that, Jackie?"

"I can't believe it! It's better than bumming you!"

He used one of the baby's napkins, cleaned the sticky goo from my belly and threw the napkin in the wash.

Unfortunately, it didn't affect my companion in quite the same way. When I caressed him, looked into his eyes and made love, it was beautiful for both of us. I filled him with my shooting stars, but he still had to take me in turn to fulfil his desire. As time passed I became the gentle one, accepted the handsome boy willingly, and finished up with a sticky belly from my own squirting spout and a slippy wet bum from his. We played our separate roles and set a fixed pattern: Eggy, the masculine lover, and I, the happy, fluttering, young sweetie beneath his firm thrusting young muscles. It just seemed natural and we liked it that way.

Things were much different on the streets. I worked very hard. Nobody could find a job of work in the whole city but I cleaned windows, trimmed hedgerows and pulled a hand-cart, loaded up like a donkey, for a grocer shop that stayed open until ten at night.

My schoolfriend didn't need to work and I'm sure his charming mother wouldn't have allowed him to slave like me. He was a real true friend, looked after the money I earned, the odd clothes that I managed to buy and the few shillings I managed to save.

MERSEY TUNNEL OPENED IN 1934 BY GEORGE V. AT THAT TIME LONGEST IN WORLD) AND SOLVED PROBLEM OF EXHAUST GAS BUILD UP.

CHAPTER FIVE

Boy Wanted

I fell fast asleep to the sound of the old Sally Army band playing "Throw Out The Lifeline" beneath my grimy bedroom window, and the noisy drunks staggering from the Gregson's Well and jeering loudly at the scarlet-jerseyed musicians.

"Spring holiday!" The glorious sunshine burst through the murky window of the tiny box-room where I slept and suddenly the little chamber was alive with glistening particles. I threw aside the ancient black-green cloak that covered me, creating yet another cloud of lustrous, shimmering particles and shiny specks from the dusty garment my grandfather had worn a thousand years ago.

"Three weeks holiday!" I shouted to the world about me, grabbing my second-hand khaki boy-scout's shorts. I pulled them up around my bottom and sneaked into my sleeping sister's bedroom to steal her plimsolls for the wonderful day ahead. The world was mine to roam at will for three whole weeks and I didn't intend wasting one beautiful second. Up the grimy jigger walls I scaled to say good morning to my little pal who lived on Charlie Redmayne's roof-top. My long-tailed friend chattered and threw his loving arms around my neck.

"Tiger nuts!" I laughed into his happy face. "You want some tiger nuts?"

Old Mrs Merrigan sold the shrunken peanuts in a little shop across the road, so I picked up two jam-jars from the dustbin, rinsed them under the garage water-tap and took them to the rag and bone shop.

A ha'penny piece changed hands as the dirty "rag and bone man" sat amongst his pile of tattered clothing, sorting the more expensive woollen garments from the cloth. Mrs Merrigan's fat sleek pussy-cats made me welcome, and the scary old witch gave me two farthing bags of tiger nuts in exchange for my precious ha'penny.

Back to the jigger walls I flew, peanuts swinging from my teeth in a stout brown paper bag, scaling the dizzy heights once more to give my grinning friend his breakfast. Red-faced Charlie waved at me so I returned his salutation, crossed the road to the centre of my universe and searched among the discarded tram tickets for a penny return that hadn't been used.

Voila! I found a penny return ticket with three rides not yet perforated by the tram conductor's punch and waited in line amidst the raucous coughing of the flat-capped generation of men who'd been gassed in the madness of the bitter trench warfare.

An empty Tizer bottle caught my eye so I rescued it from the litter bin, rinsed it at the horse trough and filled it to the very brim before returning to my place in the queue. The tramcar stopped. I climbed the stairs and sat in a little cage on the open front, far from the coughing men inside.

The noisy bell clanged and I was off on a sunny journey to meet the glorious day, water bottle in my hand and a thousand happy thoughts in my head. The rattling monster stopped again and, with a further clanging of the belt-operated bell, moved on to yet another stop. A few passengers climbed aboard, and as the tram moved off I spied a sign outside a Jewish butcher shop: "Boy Wanted!"

Suddenly a whole new world opened up. Forgetting the precious Tizer bottle in my feverish haste, I grabbed the leather strap, rang the bell and made my way down the iron staircase in search of my very first job.

The friendly kosher butcher wiped his blood-stained hands on a piece of mutton cloth and smiled at me from behind his spotless counter.

"Sir," I said respectfully, "I want the job in the window. I don't live very far from here and I'm good at getting up in the mornings."

"Can you ride a bike?" he asked, putting down the mutton cloth and making his way to my side of the counter. I knew instinctively that I had the job and told him I could ride a bike and knew every street in Liverpool. It was an old joke but I simply couldn't resist it, because Every Street *was* just around the corner, and the smiling butcher must have passed it a thousand times.

"I'll give you a trial," said the likeable man and shoved an apron over my head. It reached down to my ankles. The butcher spun me round, fastened the tapes at the back and led me into the workroom. Squawking chickens, great fat hens and crates of cackling livestock filled the smelly room from floor to ceiling.

A boy named Aaron introduced himself, a fine big curly-headed lad, fifteen or sixteen years old and brimming over with sparkling wit.

"I'll show you what we have to do all morning," he said, grabbing a squawking chicken from a crate, twisting its neck in his strong young fingers and silencing the noisy bird forever. He slapped the dead chicken on the work bench, chopped off its head and claw-like webbed feet, and tossed them into a bloodied enamel pail.

I couldn't wring the lovely chickens' necks but somehow steeled myself to chop off the heads and feet with a sharpened cleaver. Aaron emptied the pail into a huge vat and we went on to commit further atrocities to the still warm bodies: slitting the anus, shoving our hands inside and drawing out the intestines with our finges until the pail slopped over with blood and guts.

Sometime in the afternoon, Mr Hyam, the butcher, packed the delivery bike for me and sent me on the rounds. This was the life! Pedals flying, hair flowing in the breeze, cycling up and down the hills, in and out of the tram lines, stopping here and stopping there, meeting strange Jewish families and collecting a few pence in tips for being such a nice boy. I knew very little about Jewish people, although I discovered they ate much better than the folk I knew and had very beautiful children.

It was rather late when I finished my rounds, but as the shops remained open until 9 pm it didn't make much difference. Aaron helped me scrub the slaughter tables, gather up millions of feathers, stuff them in enormous sacks, and wash the blood-stained floor. "See you in the morning," he said at closing time.

"I'm not coming back," I replied. "I can't stand any more, and I'll never be able to wring a chicken's neck as long as I live."

Aaron hung the blood-stained aprons behind the door, took me to see the boss and told him all about it. The kosher butcher gave me half-a-crown and we parted company. On my way home I thought that if I managed to earn half-a-crown every day, I'd soon be a millionaire.

"Hokey Pokey ice cream!" shouted the Hokey Pokey man. I stopped beside his colourful barrow, all twists and twirls of hand-painted designs, and decided on a lump of Hokey Pokey in a cone. The home-made custard ice cream made my mouth water. He sploshed it with soft brown caramel sauce, sprinkled it with gorgeous nuts and squirted a dollop of home-made raspberry sauce on top. "Hokey Pokey, penny a lump!" shouted the Hokey Pokey man as I ran down the street, licking my sticky fingers and feeling very lucky at having spent such a glorious day.

Such riches being the root of all evil, I went scurrying off early next morning to Christie's the grocer shop where I managed to obtain a position as a delivery boy. This was a different bucket of blood altogether. The job paid three half-crowns a week and I didn't have to work every day. Consequently I could still enjoy some of the spring holiday, see my friends and earn good money.

Christie had a few delivery bikes for the lads who'd been there some time, knew their grocery business and could serve behind the counter if required. The lad who started at the bottom of the heap, however, had to earn his bicycle and deliver the goods in a hand-cart.

Hand-carts were cumbersome things and took up a lot of valuable space, so the hand-cart hiring business flourished. The pavement leading down the hill to the hand-cart depot had been used by generations of human beasts of burden, and the wheel-worn kerbstone was like a sliver of gleaming granite and sharp as a cleaver. This was caused by the time-honoured method of pressing the spinning, steel-shod wheels against it as a braking system.

Fortunately the donkey chose his own cart, so I paid the man sixpence and stepped inside the depot to get a cart for the day.

Milk floats, low loaders, bread vans as big as a house, coal carts, rag and bone carts, furniture carts and carts of every shape, size and design filled the huge depot as far as the eye could see.

I chose a cart with long-handled shafts because I'd seen the skilful way the boys in the coal yard handled them, and knew if the load was too heavy it would lift me off my feet as soon as I hit an uneven surface. The trick was to keep your eye on the road surface and move further up the shafts to create a balance, a bit like a pair of human scales. It was rather fun; you could fly down the hills, feet dangling or kicking merrily in the air as the sparks flew from the wheel-worn kerbstones.

The first day was pretty tough. It started out well enough, the cheese turner giving me lumps to taste while the manager sorted out the order in which my deliveries had to be loaded.

Thick leather harness about my chest, hands on the shafts, I moved off easily enough down Brunswick Road, the smell of John Emmett's wonderful meat pies and gravy in my nostrils and the lovely creamy taste of rich Danish cheese in my mouth.

A big fat woman – on her way to the public wash-house with the family laundry – dumped a great basket of smelly laundry on my cart and grabbed a shaft with me; such is the way of those who sweat and toil.

Obviously, the last items to be delivered were at the bottom of the cart and the first items at the top. Unfortunately, the guy who had loaded them wrote them on my list as they went aboard. Naturally enough, I started at the top of the list, but I should have started at the bottom. It was all Chinese to me, so I went about my rounds in reverse order, diving and scrambling for every package when it should have been so simple.

The beauty of pulling a hand-cart is knowing that every step you take is a step nearer to a lighter cart and that each delivery makes the burden easier. Down to the rope works, dump a packet of tallow candles, grab the back of a horse-drawn wagon to pull me across the bustling carriage-way, harness taut and tight across my chest. Up the hill to Everton Brow, clinging tightly to the wagon and horse I've commandeered for the deadly climb. A package here, and a package there; I'm doing fine and the cart gets lighter with each stop.

The smell of the home-made sweet factory hits my nose in a wash of honey, saccharine, lemon, treacle toffee and molasses. Pure cane sugar and toasted coconut smells make my mouth water and I can go no further; I simply can't pass the wonderful little factory. So I place the sturdy two-wheeled carriage by the entrance, shove a sharpened wooden chock beneath the wheels, and enter the wonder-land of Mill Road's magic sweet shop.

There is so much to choose from: great slabs of caramel toffee, toffee spiced with Devon cream and laced with walnuts, chocolate drops and chocolate nougat, mint drops, pear drops, butter drops and snow drops. The gorgeous smells make my head reel. A man in a floppy chef's hat is making bars of mint rock with his magic hands, and a boy is pulling the bright red toffee to form the tiny lettering that will finish up inside the rock and make it into a speciality: Brighton rock, Blackpool rock and all the lovely minty rocks in the world.

Desiccated coconut, toasted and golden brown, covers a long white table like a beach, and another boy is rolling warm chocolate-covered dates in the bed of fragrance. He lines each neat little roll along the edge of the table and carries on and on.

What can I choose? Bullseyes, gobstobbers, hazelnut whirls packed with fresh cream, lemon drops, tiny, tiny hundreds and thousands and beautiful, dark brown aniseed balls . . .

I choose a quarter pound of coconut stick-jaw and give the lady in the tiny retail corner my penny. The chef smiles at me and throws me a chocolate-covered almond.

Then, as I'm about to pick up my well-balanced cart to resume my journey, the almond crunches beneath my strong white teeth and I wonder if the stick-jaw was the best buy after all. I'm afraid to sink my teeth into the rock hard toffee, because I know from past experience that I'll never be able to open my mouth again.

Mill Road hospital – scarlet fever blankets and bustling nurses. I flee from the dreadful place and spy a boy like myself harnessed to a monstrous bread cart. Across the busy road we fly, past St Augustin's church and onto the new macadamised surface of Boaler Street. The smooth surface is incredible after spending the day on the granite sets that make up the city roads and highways.

A package here, a package there, and the boy with the bread van still ahead of me. I scoot along, legs kicking wildly in the air, balancing in the long-handled shafts of the almost empty cart and catch him up.

He smiles. We fly along the newly-tarred road with scarcely a rattle from the steel-shod wheels, smiling and laughing as we race to the park and stop for lunch beneath the sparse green trees.

The chip shop by the cinema beckons me so I buy a penny bag of chips and share them with the laughing bread boy who offers me a fine fresh barm cake from his monstrous carriage. Barm cake and chips! Ah! The friendly boy has many things to share and presents me with a luscious currant loaf.

He has to make his way along Sheil Road so we have to part company. I cross into Judges Drive to deliver my packages to the thin-faced housemaids in the noble judges' homes. Coal men, dust men and noisy motorbikes are prohibited in Judges Drive. Private road! No thoroughfare! No hawkers or musicians! Loiterers will be prosecuted! Keep off the grass!

At last the cart is empty and I scoot back to Mr Christie's bargain grocery store, full of pride and feeling hot and sticky.

Harnessed to my empty cart, I set off on my evening journey, candle-holding lantern swinging from the rear of my trundling carriage in case I'm held up and can't return before lighting-up time.

Through the piles of horse manure I tread, tattered plimsolls slipping in the mire, wheels rattling noisily on the granite sets and sturdy hand-cart bouncing on its steel-leafed springs to Lovell & Christmas, the great warehouse in Williamson Square.

"Below!" shouts the man on the hoist and sends a great steel hook and cable crashing to the concrete paving-slabs and to the carters waiting to unload the dockland provisions. As fast as one carter unloads his stores into the warehouse, so another carter fills his wagon and removes an equal amount of different goods. White-aproned coopers sit around in the evening sunshine, making butter barrels from wooden staves and hoops of springy timber strong as steel. Their skill amazes me. A couple of circular slabs of wood, six wooden hoops, 36 staves, and in a few minutes the cooper has a waterproof, airtight barrel.

"Below!" the voice rings in my ears.

It's my turn to take a load: ten crates of eggs for Mr Christie. The expert hoistman sets them gently on the concrete slabs and I unhook the sling. "Take it away!" I shout like all the men, and load the little cart with 3,600 new laid eggs. A friendly warehouse porter lashes them together for me and shows me how to release the intricate knot with a simple pull. 360 eggs = 1 crate. A case of tinned milk weighs 28 lb. 56 lb = a box of butter. 28 lb = a box of margarine and 112 lb is the weight of a small bag of sugar. They didn't teach me this at school, but I learn quickly. . .

I light my candle, hang the lantern from the now familiar cart and drag my way through town – past the great St George's Hall, Nelson's Column, the screaming Mary Ellens, T.J. Hughes – the bargain shop for men! Two pair of socks for sixpence! Special offer! Summer sale! A kind policeman holds up the evening traffic while I cross the busy road into Moss Street and the last stage of my journey. The stick-jaw holds me in its vice-like grip and I have to snort through my nostrils like a donkey on the long pull up Brunswick Road to the end of a perfect day.

The cheese man seems to like me, shows me how to tie the special grocer's knot and how to snap the finger-cutting twine in the most dextrous way. Before we part and say goodnight, he tells me he'll bring in a pair of shoes for me to work in. Mr Christie gives me a whole box of broken biscuits and I wend my way to my schoolfriend's home to share his bed and talk about the exciting day.

The cheese man kept his word and soled the shoes with motor-car tyre, making me half an inch taller. I'd never seen motor-car tyre used as shoe leather before but it was the ideal thing for taking a grip on the road and, of course, it cost nothing.

There were plenty of little jobs around for a willing lad, so I managed to find all kinds of ways to earn a few shillings, but my heart was in the shops and the interesting shopkeepers around me. Butchers, for example, were the happiest of men. They all had lovely fresh complexions and shouted out their wares to the passing parade: "There's a lovely leg o' lamb! What a fine piece of rump there, lady!"

Watching the road come to life fascinated me. Dalglish the pawnbroker usually started it off, especially on a Monday morning when everyone was short of money. He employed quite a few smart young men in navy blue business suits. Women and children queued up outside and waited patiently with their bundles, wedding rings, cases of cutlery and various wedding presents which were seldom used for any purpose other than a pledge.

The smart young men removed the long brown wooden shutters from the windows one by one and, as each shutter was removed, so Dalglish's window revealed its glittering display of gold, silver, diamond rings and expensive watches. The boys carried the shutters into the dim interior of the back room and the women marched into the pawn shop entrance and onto the bare black dirty floorboards with their pledges. The front entrance to the shop was completely different: thick pile carpets on the polished floor, beautiful display cabinets, and all the riches and velvet of the jewel trade laid out in great style.

A fat-faced fishmonger across the road laid out his kippers in neat little pairs. No one ever bought one kipper – kippers came in pairs and that amazed me. A cod, a mackerel or a pint of prawns, but why a pair of kippers? Nobody asked for a pair of bananas, a pair of toffee apples or a pair of coconuts. A pair of shoes, yes; but why a pair of kippers?

"Fresh fish!" bawled the fishmonger, laying bunches of parsley all over the silvery sea food. Why parsley? Why not some other bunch of fragrant herbs, and why did the butcher garnish *his* meats with parsley? Was this some ancient tradition or was there a special purpose in the display? "To keep the flies away," explained the friendly cheese man. "Parsley has some strange property which keeps the flies at a distance." It didn't seem to keep the bluebottles away and that's for sure.

Thomas the greengrocer had the most amazing display of

all, and most of it was on the pavement: coconuts and shiny apples, ripe tomatoes, rich red plums and yellow bananas, pineapples, peaches and green strings of beans, peas in the pod and bunches of beautiful flowers.

The Cow Butter store was my favourite shop because it was very old-fashioned and wouldn't change its Victorian ways for anybody.

If you wanted a half pound of butter, they chopped it with a wet butter pat, put it on a marble slab, gave it a few slaps with the wooden spatula to knock it into the required shape and finished it off with the butter pats. Then they weighed it off and made pretty country designs all over it, the final one being the trademark of the Cow Butter stores. A butter and cheese tasting section allowed you to "taste and try before you buy" and a section where they produced fresh jugs of buttermilk gave free drinks and spoonfuls of cream.

The older generation of ancient sea-dogs, grandparents and Victorian people would queue for hours at the Cow Butter stores, and yet anybody in Liverpool could walk into our shop and say, "Send a boy round to my house with six eggs and a half pound of bacon right away."

"Yes sir!" the nearest assistant would shout, and write down the address to send the delivery boy immediately. However, the older generation wouldn't accept Mr Christie's smart modern service, business style and cracked eggs at half price. Mr Christie flourished nonetheless.

By the time the Dalglish boys had hung the secondhand suits, overcoats, raincoats, top hats and bowlers from the window blinds outside the pawnshop entrance, the customers were making their Monday morning round of the shops, money in their buttoned purses and scruffy children clinging to their skirts. I do believe if Mr Dalglish had shut up shop on Mondays, the whole of Brunswick Road would be deserted, except for the Cow Butter stores of course. People still used gold sovereigns there and would not accept paper money though they would accept the inconvenience of eight silver half-crowns instead of a pound note.

John and Robert Emmett, the pork butchers, filled the streets with the most delicious smells from their cooking hams, boiling gravies, spice balls, faggots, pork pies in jelly, hand-made tomato sausage, Lincoln sausage, cooked tongues, pigs' feet, pressed veal and every cooked meat you could imagine. The only part of the pig they had no use for was its squeak.

I could take my cart down Brunswick Road and get a smile from every shopkeeper, except of course the people in the modern chemist shop who hid behind closed doors and sold the most secret little things that took me years to discover.

Mr Christie's shop had the cleanest and most sparkling window in the road but not a very grand display. "The shop window," explained the boss, "is the silent salesman. That's where all the bargains go: the cheapest goods and all the written adverts. Do you realise, young man, you are the first generation of readers in this country?"

Thick blue paper-bags for sugar, green bags for peas, green bags with a yellow stripe for split-peas and lentils. Snow-white bags for flour and yellow bags for custard powder; orange bags for spices, red and brown for coffee and light brown bags for tea. Christie's busy little shop was quite a factory.

All the goods came right from the docks: 240 lb sacks of flour, 224 lb sacks of sugar. Young girls couldn't handle the heavy goods, so Christie employed boys and young men. One boy put a scoop of sugar in a thick blue paper-bag, set it on the counter and repeated the action as another boy weighed the sugar to the point of perfection, spoon and basin near his dextrous hand. A third boy wrapped the sugar bag and packed it neatly in a nearby shelf. All the goods packaged on the premises to save money.

A sack of coffee beans cost very little but weighed a great deal and could be mistaken for a sack of soda crystals, but the brown stripe on the bag told you it was coffee; it smelt delicious going through Christie's grinding machine. 240 lb tea-chests: tea from China, India and all the tea plantations in the world packed the stockroom high.

The cheese room was a miniature warehouse. The cheeses of the world: huge, flat wheels of Brie had to lie on beds of straw, Camembert in cupboards, so they would mature. Every county in England had its own cheese: Lanca-shire white, red Leicester, Cheddar red, creamy-crumbly Cheshire, blue Stilton. . . Red balls of tough hard cheese from Holland, marbled monsters from Italy, smelly, smelly Gorgonzola, Limberger. . . beautiful cheese from France crusted with the pips of grape.

Brown stone 28 lb jars of jam were spooned into Christie's little glass jars, a tiny grease cap atop, wrapped in finger-cutting twine and producing a 500 per cent profit. Currants, raisins, dried fruits and chopped peels; all in bulk awaited the busy hands of Christie's slaves.

The wrapping and packaging took place long after 9 pm when the shop closed but Christie's slaves must carry on. Saturday night was pay night, so they wrapped and packed until after 11 pm, waiting for their wages. The manager dared not lose his job because he had a family, so he came in on his half day and slaved till midnight at the stock books. He earned the fabulous salary of almost three pounds a week, twice as much as the working coalminer.

Dirty sawdust was swept into the street and fresh clean sawdust put on the floor. Reams and reams of grease-proof paper, paper-bags behind the door. Stout brown paper-bags with good string handles were provided free, but they bore Christie's name: it pays to advertise. Each tiny sheet of grease-proof paper was weighed in along with the purchase and consequently paid for itself.

Outer wrappings, however, could not be weighed in with the goods. Therefore I had to take my trusty hand-cart to the *Echo* office, and collect them – for absolutely nothing. Into the fantastic clamour of the printing department I walked and, amidst the pounding roar of the newspaper machines, collected a thousand of last week's *Echo*. The paper weighed a ton, but the *Echo* boys pushed me up the hill to Christie's and the whole thing began once again.

"Broken biscuits, penny a pound!" Christie wasted nothing. "Empty tea-chests, sixpence each!" One could make a bedroom wardrobe from a couple of tea-chests. But now a new exciting store opened up in Brunswick Road – "The Co-op shop. Discounts in cash!" "Hop! Hop! Hop! To the Co-op shop. . ." sang the scruffy kids. "Free bacon bones for all!" retaliated Mr Christie's sign in business-like revenge. The daily battle of the high street filled my life with wonder.

CHAPTER SIX

A Week in the Country

During the long summer holidays I managed to get hold of an old secondhand bike, worked on it and made it look like new. It made me feel proud and filled me with satisfaction.

Eggy had gone to Cornwall to stay with his grandma for the holidays. Although he would only be away for a month, it made us very unhappy. Suddenly the world seemed empty, and I felt all alone.

Some of the older boys now asked me to go camping with them, accepting me as one of their own because I had a bike and pulling the heavy handcart had made me big, husky and strong.

A wealthy kid (his family owned a small pub) named Johnny Fitz had become very friendly with me. He was about sixteen and it was at his suggestion that I was invited on the camping holiday.

"I'd love to go with you, Johnny. What do we do about food?"

"We cook our own," he said. "Bring a tin of sugar, some cocoa and some tea. My mam will give me plenty of money for eggs and bacon, and we can get vegetables and potatoes from the farmers for almost nothing. You'll need a blanket, a towel and all the spare underwear and shirts you can carry. You'll enjoy it, Jackie. Don't worry – I'll look after you. I'm a good camper and a smashin' cook."

We were quite a mixed bunch: one twelve year old schoolboy, a public house busker, a seventeen year old pianist, a young bartender, one brilliant electrician and an unemployed youth of eighteen who told jokes from the moment he opened his eyes until he fell asleep. I found it very hard to believe that these nice friendly lads came from stinking hovels such as mine. But they did. . . even Johnny Fitz! His public house was a dreadful hole and the family accommodation just as bad. I'd slept at his home with his younger brother Gerry and fleas had jumped and crawled all over us.

Teddy was a real big boy: six foot tall, strong as an ox, very handsome and masculine-looking. He worked at the Automatic factory and helped to produce the new telephone system and traffic lights that were springing up all over the country. Teddy seemed to be the most experienced camper and had his own tent, inflatable bed, collapsible primus stove, great thick quilted sleeping-bag and all kinds of modern things, including a miniature radio that he'd built himself. We told him that it wouldn't work, but he assured us that it would work anywhere and that we would be able to listen to amateur radio enthusiasts talking to us all night long.

Stevie was seventeen, had a guitar, a voice like an angel and earned a living by shoving his foot in a public house doorway, strumming his guitar and singing yodelling songs. After ten minutes or so, he would stroll among the drunken bums in the ale-house, cap in hand, collect a few pieces of silver and move on to the next corner pub to entertain the drunks there. Liverpool pubs couldn't get music licences. The Licenced Victuallers Association did not want their customers opening their mouths to sing; they wanted them scoffin' ale.

Bernie was the unemployed lad with the head full of jokes and Micky was the pianist who travelled from town to town and played the piano at different social gatherings, weddings and late night parties.

Johnny's tent was so big and heavy that we had to send it ahead by rail, so we threw in the heavy cooking utensils and larger pieces of equipment, including a 7 lb axe for chopping logs. I got terribly excited at the thought of chopping trees, building our own camp fire and cooking our own food but the big lads seemed to take it all in their stride.

We set off on our bikes, six of us, loaded down with camping gear. It was my first journey out of the city and I felt that it would be the greatest adventure of my life. I fell in behind the bigger boys and was pleased to see the guitar slung across Stevie's fine young shoulders. I had often followed him on his rounds and looked forward to hearing him singing at our camp fire.

We had ridden about ten miles along the East Lancashire road when Bernie called a halt. "Sniff up lads! We're in the country! Time for a piss and a bite to eat."

Teddy stood beside me, peeing in the bushes. It was the first time I'd ever seen a boy with such a great thick dickie and I couldn't take my eyes off it. My own pigeon stiffened up, and Teddy smiled at me.

"Is this the first time you've been camping?" asked the handsome young man.

"Yes," I replied, blushing like mad as his enormous penis grew longer and longer before my very eyes. "Do we have far to go?"

"Another fifteen miles," said the young giant, forcing the great monster back into his shorts. "Let's have a drink of Tizer."

Unfortunately, the bottles of pop had got warm in the heat of the summer's day. "I think we should move on," suggested Bernie. "We can call at one of the farms for a cold drink. This stuff's piss poor."

"Sounds like a fuckin' good idea," replied Stevie, slinging his guitar over his shoulder, climbing onto his bike and waiting for me to couple up with him as we rode two abreast. He had bright green eyes. I'd never seen green eyes before. They made him look very handsome and attractive. "Are you going to give us a few songs tonight?" I asked him, sitting tall in the saddle and riding "no hands". "I've heard you busking round the pubs and I think you have the best voice I've ever heard."

"You wanna hear a few songs like that?" asked the green-eyed boy. "Wait till tonight. Micky's gonna play the piano in the boozer on the canal bank, and I'm gonna yodel my head off. We'll have a fuckin' marvellous time."

Every yard we rode seemed to get more exciting than the last. It was like being in a foreign country; the people spoke a different language and I could only guess what they were saying. We stopped at an old-fashioned farm house and asked for water.

"Wheeeare dust thee kumm fra?" asked the fat-faced farmer. "Thee's nobbut weerin' clogs lakk t'other lads yon!"

"We come from Liverpool!" we shouted. "Liverpool!

Where only the bugs wear clogs!"

He gave us glasses of cool, refreshing home-made wine, and let us help ourselves to the ripe juicy plums and hard green apples that grew in his orchard. I couldn't believe it really. I wasn't stupid and knew perfectly well that fruit grew on trees. . . yet I felt in my heart and soul that it was not possible! Fruit came up from the docks in boxes and crates. Yet here it was – right before my very eyes: pears, apples, plums and raspberries that you didn't have to steal! The old farmer had new potatoes, fresh vegetables and long fat juicy marrows. I wondered if the magic man grew his own coconuts and bananas!

We climbed aboard our laden bikes and the fat old farmer rubbed his dusty hands on his apron. "Fare thee well!" he shouted. "Lukk after thee sen!"

We said goodbye in our hard Liverpool accents and carried on with the journey.

"Gear ole fucker, wannee?"

"Yer! Fucken' gear! Pity he cudden speak the King's fucken English!"

"Fuck the King!"

"I'd sooner fuck the Prince of Wales."

On we went, packs digging into our backs, bright green fields all around, lovely crystal clear streams and big bushy hedgerows. It was simply breathtaking for me. I had seen plenty of cattle in the slaughterhouse – seen their bleeding hides, smelt them and seen the rivers of blood in the drains. The horses that I knew were harnessed to the shafts of some great heavy cart, and the only sheep I'd seen were dead ones. As for pigs, I'd seen plenty of pig's heads in the butcher shops but never one running about and squealing.

I saw plenty of real live animals this day: hundreds of the beautiful creatures, grazing in the lush green fields; goats, real live goats with horns! I thought a goat was some kind of mountain animal and almost died when a farmer's girl offered me a cup of goat's milk.

"No thank you!" I said. "Definitely not! I couldn't possibly!"

"Give him some cow's milk," said the girl's father. "'Tis not every day yon city lads has nanny's milk, lass."

However, one look at the cow shit all over the farm yard

and the filthy brown-stained cow's tail, unwashed tits and dirty hooves was enough for me. I just would not drink the milk. Bernie tried to persuade me. "No thanks!" I said quite firmly. "I'll drink milk out of a botle or out of a tin but I'm fuckin' sure I won't drink that stuff!"

Previously I had enjoyed a fried egg. . . if I was lucky enough to get one. I knew all about eggs; I carried crates of them all night long when I worked with my handcart. However, seeing them in the farmer's chicken house, still warm and specked with chicken shit, put me off eggs for the rest of my life.

Eventually we reached a tiny canal-side village called Gathurst. "This is the place," said Johnny, letting go of his handlebars and riding "no hands" alongside me. "Wait until you see the camp site, Jackie. It's not a recognised camping ground, but there's a shop that has everything we need. There's a river for swimming, trees to climb and everything you could wish for!"

All the gear we'd sent on ahead was waiting for us at the camp shop. Johnny bought half a dozen candles, paid the man sixpence for the use of his camping ground and slung the big tent over his shoulder. "You carry the poles and cooking pot," he said. "Follow me. We're going to camp on top of the hill. That's the first lesson in camping. Only fools camp on low ground."

The musical lads carved a huge square sod from the turf, rolled it up and laid it out flat behind a bush. They seemed to know what they were doing, but it was mystery to me so I helped erect the big tent while Stevie and his mate chopped up some logs and built a fire on the earthen square. Big Teddy and the other guy rigged up the smaller tent, piled in all the cycle bags and clothing and filled it with everything except bedding.

"That's the store tent," said Johnny. "Give me your blanket and I'll rig up a bed for us two. It gets cold in the night so you can share my sleeping-bag. The others will all be doubling up. "

Everybody stripped off for a swim. "Don't be shy," said Johnny, wrapping a towel round his waist. "We always swim in the nude. There's no one around here – only the squirrels in the tree tops." I wasn't shy at all! I was just amazed at the size of these big naked lads. I had thought of them as youths and boys but they were full grown men with great long hanging testicles, big thick dickies and great bushes of pubic hair. I had only been with my schoolfriend and thought I had a decent sized pigeon until I saw this lot. There was no comparison! However, I joined in the fun and we ran to the river in our towels.

That night we camped beneath the summer sky. The moon and stars reached down and touched us, kissed our happy faces and returned to twinkle above our heads, spinning, flickering and dancing heel toe, gleaming in the heavens above.

Woodsmoke from our camp fire drifted in, and we smelled the new-mown hay and dew-damp grass, heard the ripple of the woodland stream and the rushing waters where we had swum, dived, climbed into the highest branches of the trees and dived again and again.

I snuggled up to Johnny and put my arm around him. He was a very friendly, handsome boy and I liked him. One of the boys climbed over us, walked over to the dying camp fire and stood there naked in the firelight's glow. He looked magnificent, the light dancing on his brown belly and muscular chest. It looked like Stevie but I wasn't sure in the dim light. He had a sexy great erection; he took hold of it, directed it at the bushes and peed. The sparkling steady stream went right over the bushes and it made me very horny just looking at the squirting organ. Afterwards he climbed over us very carefully and slid into bed with his partner.

Johnny was so close that I could hear his jaws chomping at his chewing-gum. My bare toes touched his, quite by accident. Johnny put his hand lightly on my waist. Our noses almost touching, he whispered, "Are you glad you came with us?"

"Yes," I replied quietly. "It's like a dream! I had no idea that it would be as lovely as this." Johnny had sparkling blue eyes and I wished I could see them. I wanted to kiss him and hoped he would squeeze me and kiss my lips. His soft fragrant hair mingled with my own black locks on the makeshift pillow and our bare chests touched; I could feel his heartbeats on my sun-browned skin. I had to draw away from him in case he felt my stiffened dickie and would think that I was just a little different. I knew exactly what I was and had an idea that big Teddy and his horny sleeping companion were up to something, but I couldn't be sure. Johnny's warm chest drew me to him like a magnet. Our stiffened pigeons touched and he held me tight.

"Sorry," I whispered in his nice warm hair. "I guess I'm horny."

"So am I," replied the gorgeous young man, sliding his hand into my knickers and resting it on my bare bottom. "I'm horny for you."

My arm went sliding down his back, and my hand rested on his bum. "You're a lovely friend," I whispered, kissing him lightly on the tip of his nose. Johnny held me very tight and his great dickie was hurting my belly. "Do you like being kissed, Jackie?" he said quietly.

"Yes," I whispered. "I'm just like you."

"I want to get up you, Jackie!"

He kissed me very lightly on the lips. I held him close, kissed him and let him take my knickers down. "Turn round," he whispered, struggling from his cotton shorts. "Turn round and let me up you!"

I had hold of his great thick pigeon in both my hands. It was just too ridiculous and I knew it would make me scream.

"Let's just play with each other," I said, stroking the lovely hard thing and pushing my own little stiff pigeon against his belly.

Johnny put his finger in my bottom, pulled me close and kissed me. "You're a lovely little peach," he said. "Turn round! Turn round! I'm going to get right up you. You'll love it!"

"No!!"

"For Christ's sake! What's the matter with you?" he whispered angrily.

"Leave me alone, Johnny. Let's just have a little cuddle. You can rub it on my belly. I don't want you up me."

"I can't understand you," he said, pushing his wet finger further into me. "You like that, don't you?"

"Yes, it's nice," I whispered. "Do you want me to do that to you?"

"No!" said Johnny, getting mad. "I want to fuck you!

You've had it up before today, I can tell!"

"You don't understand, Johnny. I'm not a bum boy," I said. "I just like being with you." We kissed for quite a long time, played with the sexy swords and fenced on our bellies until the sticky fluid shot all over us. I was glad he hadn't forced it. The amount of thick fluid that shot from him was staggering; mine was just a thin minim.

I had not had a big boy up my bottom. I wanted it badly but the size of it scared me. I had kissed my friend the policeman all over, rubbed my cheek along the side of his nice hard dickie and kissed the pubic hairs on his belly, but he had not tried to put it up my bum. He wanted to. I knew that much from experience.

The morning sunshine brought the flies and wasps out. Butterflies winged their way around the colourful wild flowers, and the smell of our morning hot cocoa drifted to my nose. Johnny was stuck to me like glue. I had to awaken him and peel our bellies apart in case we tore the skin. The boiling cocoa hung from a metal bar over the fire but there was no sign of Teddy and Stevie.

The other two were fast asleep so Johnny and I ran down to the river stark naked, towels swinging in our hands.

Two girls paddling a canoe watched us as we swam. One of them paddled closer. The other seemed shy and didn't use her paddle but she had a good look at my friend's dickie as he dried himself on the river bank. I stood behind a bush. Girls just scared me. They didn't affect me sexually. I could look at a lovely schoolboy and get horny for him, but girls made me shudder.

"What's it like in the water?" shouted the girl with the paddle.

"Get your drawers off and jump in!" shouted handsome Johnny Fitz. "You'll find out then."

They paddled off as we walked slowly up the hill. Johnny stopped me halfway up the grassy slope and looked me straight in the eyes. "Answer me truthfully," he said, holding me lightly by the shoulders. I was quite naked, towel in hand. He wore a towel round his waist. "Will you answer me truthfully?" he went on like a hypnotist. "Have you had it up you?"

"Yes. I've had it up me plenty of times, Johnny."

"Right!" said the boy, laughing all over his face. "I thought as much. Sleep with me tonight and I will get right up you."

My shrivelled-up pigeon grew stiff and I had to wear the towel. "I hate to disappoint you, Johnny," I said, feeling mean and miserable. "But it's not possible. I had sex with my schoolfriend. He had a cock like mine and we didn't hurt each other, but that monster of yours will make me scream!" I put my arm round his shoulder. "I'll sleep with you," I said. "I'll sleep with you all through the holiday, because I like being with you. It was lovely when you kept kissing and cuddling."

"Good!" said the friendly boy, putting his arm round me. "I'll be up you tonight."

"You can try!"

"I fuckin' well will," said my friend, racing me up the hill.

Steve and big Teddy had six cups of steaming hot cocoa waiting quietly on a flat log. Stevie was throwing sausages into a big black steaming pot. I poked my nose into the pot. "Fuckin' hell!" said I in loud voice. "Is that our breakfast?" Stevie looked quite annoyed. "That's fuckin' breakfast, fuckin' dinner and fuckin' tea! I'm the cook today and there's fuck all wrong with spuds, carrots, turnips, corned beef and bleedin' sausages!!!" He gave the tasty stew a mix with a big wooden spoon. "You and Bernie are washing up!"

Teddy brought a handful of mixed herbs from the store tent and threw the whole lot into the bubbling mess. "Shake the other two lazy buggers," he said as if he was the boss of the camp. "The cocoa is getting cold."

I went into the big tent to wake Bernie and the seventeen year old pianist; they were stark naked and clinging together just like I always clung to my own friend Eggy. I knew right away that they loved each other and felt mean having to disturb them. "Cocoa's ready," I said quietly.

"Mmmm!!!" murmured young Micky. "What did you say, Jackie?"

"Teddy told me to wake you up."

Micky grabbed me and we rolled over the bedding, laughing and squealing. His dickie was as thick as my young wrist and stood up like a giant tree-trunk. He finished up on top of me. I was squealing and choking with laughter because he kept tickling me. I didn't care about anything now because it was very obvious that they were all nice, friendly boys. Micky kissed me full on the lips. "Did you enjoy sleeping with Johnny?" he asked.

I struggled and tried to get away. "You're a horny sod," I shouted. "What do you want to know for?"

Micky gave me another kiss and pressed the big oak tree into my belly. "You're as pretty as a girl," said the musician. "If Johnny doesn't please you then I will!"

His friend Bernie rolled from the sleeping-bag, horny as a rhino, and dragged a pair of khaki shorts over his bottom. "Stop pissin' about," he said. "You'll pull the friggin' tent down."

Micky let me go and I scrambled from the tent on my hands and knees.

Once the morning erections had died down and everybody had taken a few slugs of Teddy's cocoa, things had to be sorted out: plans made for the day, wood chopped, shopping fetched from the farmers and, most important of all, dinner!

Stevie picked up the big ladle and held it over the pot. "Shall I serve it out now?" he asked in his normal friendly manner.

"Suits me," said the horny boy who'd kissed me ten minutes ago.

"And me," said Johnny Fitz. "What about you Bernie?"

Bernie poked his head out of the tent. "I'm starving!" he shouted back.

"Right!" said the green-eyed boy. "Line up with the fuckin' plates. Any complaints and I won't be responsible for my actions. Don't forget Jackie, you and Bernie are washing up."

The sausage and corned-beef stew was the most wonderful meal I'd eaten in my life.

Johnny and Micky went in search of some logs while Bernie and I washed up. He was a fine big lad and a million laughs, but he didn't tease me or tell any of his usual dirty jokes, nor did he make the sexy remarks that the lads usually made when we were all together. It was as if he had more respect for my youth than the others. I couldn't quite figure him out but I knew he was madly in love with Micky, no matter how tough and masculine he pretended to be with his continual wisecracks and sexy jokes about girls.

Stevie and Teddy went off to Wigan for the day to see Harold Lloyd in a new talking picture. Micky decided to spend the day fishing with his friend. Johnny said he'd like to swim to Wigan along the canal if I would go with him, and the other two said they'd meet us later in the evening at an old canal-side pub called the Navigator. Unfortunately, the heavy dinner-cum-breakfast-cum-tea we'd eaten had made swimming a thing to be postponed for a few hours, so I lay in the sunshine with Johnny for most of the day. It was quiet and peaceful when we finally stirred ourselves. Johnny seemed to have given up his sexual bombardment but I hoped he hadn't given up completely because I really wanted to try it out.

"How about our swim?" I asked the naked young sex-pot. "Are you ready?"

"Okay. Let's put some shorts on. Wigan's a fuckin' town. We can't swim there bollock naked. Do you think you can make it?"

"I'll keep up with you," I assured him. "If I can't, then you can do whatever you want when we get to bed."

"Let's go!" he shouted, running down the hill.

"Do we need towels?" I shouted to his retreating back.

"Don't be daft!" he replied over his shoulder. "How can you swim with a towel in your silly fuckin' hand?"

We swam the three miles in the smelly canal and walked back along the bank, sans-souci, singing our heads off and skimming flat pebbles across the filthy water. Unfortunately, they wouldn't let us in the "Navvy" so we ran back to camp, put some fresh logs on the fire and prepared to make our supper.

Johnny was a mine of information. I learned a few things that seemed quite important at the time and yet they were so simple. "One log on a fire," said my friend, "will smoulder for a while, and then simply die out. Two logs, touching side by side, will burn brightly, but three logs will cause smoke and sparks to fly. You must always separate the logs before you turn in for the night."

With that wonderful load of information in my childish mind, I replied: "I wonder what the lads are doing?"

"Getting pissed on cider," answered Johnny producing a big carving knife.

"What's that for?" I enquired.

"You'll see," said Johnny proudly.

"Open a few tins of stew and sling them in the pot. The lads will be hungry when they get back."

The stew was bubbling away merrily and the boy was chopping sticks of celery with the carving knife. "Sling that lot in," he said. "I'm going to make some suet dumplings."

He piled a little heap of flour onto the chopping block, made it into a volcano shape and shredded some suet into the hole.

"You might have washed your hands first," I said, watching him rub the flour and suet in his fingers.

"Don't worry about it," he said, adding a little milk, rolling the sticky mess into small golf-sized balls in his floury hands and dropping them one by one into the steaming cauldron. "I'm making a special supper for us two," he added. "Break three or four eggs and whisk 'em together, Jackie. I'll make a fuckin' camp-fire cook out of you yet."

Johnny chopped some onions and threw them in a giant-sized frying pan, added some finely-chopped raw potato, and sprinkled salt and pepper on top. "Let's have a little cuddle in the tent?" he said, putting a lid on the frying pan. "When the onions have simmered down you can sling the eggs in."

I fancied a little cuddle. Unfortunately, he wanted a lot more. "For Christ's sake wait until bedtime!" I shouted. "The boys might be back any minute."

Back outside, he grated some cheese, mixed it with the eggs and poured the sloppy mess into the frying pan.

"It looks fuckin' awful!" I said.

"Wait till it rises," said Johnny. "You'll love it. I've saved a bit of butter for your bum. I'm going up you tonight!"

"If I let you," I reminded him.

The smell from the frying pan was absolutely delightful. The golden brown mixture rose up like a beautiful, mouth-watering soufflé and we scoffed it right from the pan. The boys arrived about ten minutes later to find us sitting side by side on a log, towels round our waists and bellies full of camp-fire omelette.

They filled their plates with stew, wolfed the whole lot and sat around the fire singing to Stevie's guitar. Someone put another log on the fire and we sat around for hours telling dirty jokes. It was marvellous!

After a while, when the night became chilly and the dew was glistening in the cold damp grass, we separated the logs and crept into our warm nests. Johnny held me close and took my knickers down.

"Wait until they have been for a pee," I whispered. Sure enough, Micky got up and stood in the firelight's glow, squirting the secondhand cider over the bushes in a silvery stream.

Holding my friend's big pigeon in both hands simply thrilled me, but I thought they would all want to be up me if they saw Johnny doing it, so I held back. Johnny kissed and sucked at my boyish nipple, nuzzled my ear and crawled up into a crazy position, rubbing his smooth bottom against my face.

"Stoppit!" I whispered, pinching his bum.

"What's the matter?" asked Johnny. "Don't you like my bottom?"

"Not in my face!"

He snuggled down and we kissed a few times. I liked him very much because he kept saying nice things to me until I sighed with pleasure. His bottom stuck in my face once more, I pinched it and made him squeal. "Stop it, Johnny. . . just love me."

He wanted my face near his bottom for some reason or other, and when he realised that I didn't understand why, Johnny slid under me and kissed my bottom right on the most intimate spot.

"Did you like that?" he whispered.

"Yes."

"More?"

"Yes . . . it was lovely."

His lips hovered over me and I felt his warm breath almost inside me. Then he kissed me and made me slippy with his pointed tongue. "Do it to me," whispered the sexy boy.

"No! Definitely not!"

"Don't get mad," he said. The darting tongue went right inside me and made me sigh with pleasure.

"More, Johnny! More!"

"Tongue or cock?" asked Johnny. I just wriggled, and pushed my bottom near his face. "Get on your knees," he whispered. "Out of the sleeping bag and on your knees. I want to put my tongue right inside!"

"Don't get up me. I'm not ready for you, Johnny. Give it a couple more days then you can do it," I said, not quite sure of myself.

"I won't fuck you, Jackie," he whispered. "I'll wait until you ask me first. I promise." I felt mean, becase I knew what it was like to be horny for a boy you like.

"Let me go?" I asked him nicely. "I need a pee!" I thought of peeing on the camp fire but changed my mind and peed right over the bushes. It felt wonderful! "My first great big boy!" I said aloud. "I wonder what it will feel like having that great thing pumping into me?"

The cool wind blew gently on my skin and the stars twinkled above my head in the soft summer's night. A train hurtled through the darkness, steam whistling in the still night air, and the rails rattled in the distance. Owls in the nearby tree-tops made strange scary sounds and a scurrying night creature frightened me.

"You're cold," said my friend as I slipped in between the loose blanket covering. I kissed him gently on his lips.

"Here's the butter!" I said shyly.

"Can I go all the way?" asked Johnny in the darkness of the tent.

"Yes," I replied. "Don't hurt me. . . please. . . it's very big and stiff."

The slippy tongue began its work, then the butter and Johnny. . . Big! Big! Johnny!

"I'm up you!" whispered the lad to my kneeling body. "Right up! You're beautiful! It went in easy!"

"It hurts!" I protested over my shoulder. "Please take it out!"

"You'll get used to it!"

"Please. . . !"

"I'm sorry," he whispered, removing the monstrous thing from my body. "Will you let me try again? I want to finish what we've started."

Someone made a sleepy boy's sound. Johnny held me

close. "Nothing to worry about," he assured me. "They're all fast asleep. Can I try again?" he asked in his friendly voice.

"I don't mind," I whispered in his ear. "Go for the works!"

"Is that better?" asked my friend after he'd entered a second time. The only thing that bothered me this time was his stamina. I wanted it to last forever and wondered how long he could keep it up. "Are you happy now?" he asked.

"Yes," I whispered, genuinely relieved. "You're a lovely big boy, Johnny. Keep it going!" I thought about the other lads, and hoped that Micky would ask to do it next time he wrestled on the blankets with me.

"You were a real peach!" he said when he had finished. "Do you want to spunk off now?"

"It's too late," I replied. "I've already come! It's gone all over your sleeping-bag. I'm sorry."

"Mine didn't go on the sleeping-bag," said Johnny, "and I'm not sorry!"

We cuddled down and he stroked my face until I fell asleep in his arms. I just wanted more and more after that. Some nights he made me bleed but I didn't care. I just needed a man and there was nothing I could do about it.

Something drew me to Johnny, and I think it was the kind and gentle way he treated me in bed. When we stood at the water's edge and he discovered that he'd made me bleed, the gentle boy shed tears.

"Don't worry about it," I said, trying to sound confident and mature. "A few minutes in the river will soon stop the bleeding. The cold water will fix it. I want to be with you again tonight, Johnny."

Words of love came naturally to us and yet we were only children. By the time our camping holiday was at an end, I simply could not do without him.

But end it did, unfortunately. Micky and Bernie brushed away all the wood ash, tucked it down a rabbit hole, picked up the great sod of earth from behind the bushes and rolled it back into its original place. There was not a trace left of our wonderful holiday.

CHAPTER SEVEN

Me and My Man

Without Eggy, life became unbearable. I missed my school-friend and his nice clean home. Johnny worked all the hours that God sent and my friendly camping companions had their own lives to live. Besides, what would they do with a schoolboy hanging around? They didn't wish to be seen with a young lad like me.

I could have spent my time playing in the park or swimming like the other kids I knew, but I wanted a man! I needed a man! I needed a man just as desperately as Juliet needed Romeo, or a wife needed a husband. There were boys who almost begged me to play cricket and football with them because it was part of our daily life, but I just searched for a friendly face. I made myself as nice and presentable as possible and walked all over town.

I went as far as hiding a bottle of shampoo behind the ventilator in the swimming baths where I spent the first hour of each day, swimming, shampooing my hair, showering then going into town in search of a man. I think I would have gone with anyone who wanted a nice young boy to love. Fortunately I bumped into the right one. I didn't recognise him at first because he was in uniform. He stopped the traffic and called me to him. "Jackie!" he said. "Do you still remember me?"

"How could I ever forget you, Eddie? It's not so long ago."

"You stopped calling on me . . .?"

"I must go," I interrupted. "I can't explain now but I still have your key. I'll let myself into your home and wait for you, I promise. Do you want me still?"

"You still care . . .?"

"You know I do, Eddie. I always will," I said, tears almost filling my eyes.

"You've grown so big and strong!" he said.

"Please, Eddie, let me go?" I said. "People are looking at us." The traffic was piling up and it was a busy crossroads. "I'll be there!" I called and ran away from him in tears.

I was waiting for him: sitting in his living-room and enjoying a programme on the radio, tea by my side and shoes in the vestibule doorway in case I spoiled his nice clean carpets. His face lit up when he saw me. He removed his helmet and I thought he would hug me close but he didn't. He rumpled my hair and ran up the stairs. I followed him to his room and sat on his bed while he changed.

"I hope you don't mind me sitting on your bed," I said, as friendly as possible. "But I've been waiting to see you for almost an hour. I made myself a cup of tea. I hope you don't mind."

"Of course not!" he replied. "God! You've grown up! How old are you now?"

"I'll soon be thirteen," I said proudly.

"You look about fifteen!" replied the handsome man. "I've never stopped thinking about you. . . You were like a son to me. Why didn't you call? Did I offend you?"

He was almost naked by this time. I could see he was embarrassed and wanted to take a bath or use the portable shower I'd seen while nosing around. "Do you mind if I get out of these shorts?" he asked. "I'm hot and dusty and I need a shower. I've been among the traffic all day long." I laughed along with him as he removed his shorts.

"Don't mind me," I said. "I'm growing up. I've seen plenty of guys with no clothes on. I'll come and wash your hair if you like. I'd like things to be just as they were when we first became friends."

His long pointed dickie began to rise and he covered it with his hand as he went to the bathroom. I followed him in and watched him grow hard and stiff as he turned on the taps.

Eddie smiled at me. "You're making me feel embarrassed," he said. "Be a good boy and go and settle down in the living-room. You can make me a pot of tea if you want to do something useful."

I had another quick look at my photograph by his bedside and it brought back memories of my happy day at the circus. The handsome boy in the photo looked like a stranger to me.

He was dressed so well and looked so very smart in his nice clothes that I couldn't believe it was really me.

A few minor changes had taken place in Eddie's kitchen: modern gadgets, automatic tin-opener, an electric toaster and things I'd only seen on the movies. All I had to do was put a few spoons of tea in the pot and it was all over. However, I remembered how Eggy's mother used to serve the tea, so I laid everything out on a big silver tray, switched the electric kettle on, waited until I heard him leave the bathroom and filled the tea-pot.

When he came downstairs and saw the tray all nice and neat in the living-room, he remarked sadly, "My mother used to do it like that but she's dead now so I don't bother. There's not much point when you live alone."

"Why don't you get married?" I asked, pouring some milk into the cups.

"I don't know," he replied. "I don't seem to have time for things like that. Anyway, people seem to shy away from bobbies."

"I suppose you're right," I said, handing him a cup of tea. I wanted him to hold me but he seemed a little nervous so I sat beside him on the settee and asked when he was supposed to report back for duty.

"It's Sunday tomorrow," I said, smiling at him. "I suppose you have to work every day."

Eddie rumpled my hair again so I threw him one of my very best smiles and winked at him. He seemed more at ease after we had sipped a cup of tea. I winked at him again and he started laughing. "You can give me a hug," I said quite impudently. "I won't fall to pieces you know!"

He grabbed at my shoulders and hugged me close. "You still like me?" he asked in a whisper.

"Like you!" I replied. "You were the first kind person in my life. You kissed me and looked after me. I used to mention you every night in my prayers but I've stopped saying them now."

His lips touched my forehead. "You should never have stopped seeing me. Are they looking after you at home?"

"No," I replied. "I've got a little job and I've learned to look after myself. I'm doing swell! I was too ashamed to call on you until now."

We listened to the radio and enjoyed each other's company. He was a very good chess player, and was surprised to find that I played a strong attack. "Your game has improved tremendously!" he said in admiration. "You must play quite a lot!"

"My schoolfriend gives me a game," I admitted. "We got a book from the library and discovered that chess was almost as good as playing football. We really got stuck into it," I said, warming up to his friendly chatter. "Eggy – that's my pal's name – can finish a game in three moves. He's a wizard!"

Eddie knew that I was happy with him but he kept glancing at the clock. I set the chessmen out again, as the voice over the radio said, "Good evening, ladies and gentlemen. Here is the ten o'clock news."

"When do you have to be home?" enquired Eddie.

"When do you want me to go?" I replied over the chess board.

"You must have to get home sometime tonight!"

"I don't have to be home at all."

"What did you say?" asked Eddie.

I danced around the living-room shouting, "I don't have to be home at all! My ma thinks I'm still off camping with my mates. I'm supposed to be staying another week."

Eddie looked quite serious. "Do you mean you can stay with me? Is that what you're trying to tell me?" he asked.

"If you want me, Eddie."

"If I want you!" shouted Eddie. "Hell! I want you to stay forever!" We came naturally into a friendly embrace.

"My bike's in the garage! Go and see for yourself. It's loaded up with camping gear. We'll be quite safe," I assured him. I felt quite wicked actually and blushed at my own audacity but I cared for him, needed a man, and this was the one for me. He went in search of a pair of pyjamas for me.

"How long am I staying?" I asked when he returned.

"As long as you like," replied Eddie. "You might find these pyjamas about ten sizes too large but you'll manage, I'm sure. I don't have to be on duty again until Monday night and even then I'll be home every day of the week. I think we shall have time to get to know each other again, don't you?"

He sounded all excited, but not as excited as me. However,

I didn't like it one little bit when he showed me to the spare room overlooking the colourful back garden. Perhaps he was still afraid of his feelings getting the better of him. The pyjamas looked ridiculous on me, so I went downstairs, got the chessmen, came back and knocked at his bedroom door. It seemed so stupid! I knew he wanted me.

"Come in!" he called. "What's the matter? Can't you sleep?"

"No – it's a bit scary in there," I said, hitching the daft-looking pants up around my chest. "Can we sit up in your bed and play chess?"

Eddie got out of bed and took the chess board from me. His big erection stood up firm and stiff, poking at the thin pyjama covering. "You know what will happen if we sleep together," he said.

It was too much for me, so I pulled the silly jacket from me, stepped out of the oversized trousers and jumped into his bed in my knickers. He got in beside me and stroked my hair. I just melted in his big strong arms and wouldn't listen to all his silly talk. I knew perfectly well he wanted me.

"Hush! Hush!" he kept saying. "You'll be alright. . . You'll be alright. . . " He pushed the damp curls from my forehead and I kissed him, just as I always had in the past – burying my head in his stomach and stroking the side of my face with his dickie.

"I care for you," he whispered tenderly.

He must have felt my dickie pressed hard against his, so I kissed him on the forehead. His nose was smooth and his lips were smooth, but I knew his cheek would feel bristly so I didn't kiss his face.

"Take my knickers down," I whispered, kissing his smooth brown chest, struggling with the cord of his pants and doing my best to take them from him.

"You're so beautiful!" he kept saying. "Are you sure you know what you're doing?"

"We've done these things before, Eddie," I whispered. "I'm your boy. Take my knickers off! Take them right off and love me! I want you! I want you to love me."

He stroked my head very gently, and I held his dickie to my lips and kissed it. "I haven't changed," I whispered to his pubic hair.

Eddie pulled my knickers down, threw the covers from us, and looked at my nice little black triangle.

"Take your pyjamas off!" I asked him. "I can't untie the silly cord." Eddie threw his pants on the floor and we cuddled, lovely and warm. "What do you think of my nice little patch of hairs?" I asked proudly. "Do you like me in the nude?"

His big hard pigeon was slippy so I touched it, wet my finger with the warm love juice and placed it to my lips. It felt wonderful, tasting his fluid for the first time.

"You don't know what you're doing," he said getting excited.

"I do. I do," I replied. "You always wanted to put it in me and I always said no when you tried, but now I'm saying yes! You want me for your boy, don't you Eddie?"

"Yes, yes! You know I do!" he said.

"Well, I want you to be my man! Do it to me, Eddie! Do it properly!" I gripped the big stiff pole and gave it a hard squeeze.

Eddie kept saying silly things but I wanted him. I had to let him know. Clear fluid oozed from his horny organ. I deliberately wet my bottom with it and knelt on the bed with my legs open.

"Do it!" I said, gripping his great monster, wetting my bottom again and pulling him to me.

"You've changed so much," said Eddie, getting excited. "You've done these things before." His sticky belly pressed against my bottom and I knew he was going into me. "You've had it before!"

"Only from my schoolfriend," I lied. "He was only a boy like me."

"Hold still! Hold still!" shouted the excited man. "Am I hurting?"

"No! No! It's making me happy. I care for you, Eddie. You've got what you wanted at last!" I pushed back for more.

"Hold still!" he said a bit more quietly.

"Happy now, Eddie?" I asked, pushing and working in rhythm with the husky young man.

"I'm afraid. . . "

"Just love! Love me and make us both happy. I like it! Do it harder! Love me. . . "

"I am loving you! Christ! What's come over you? I love you so much!" he shouted. "I never meant to go this far. . . You're so young!"

His soft twisty hairs tickled my bum and it was lovely. He pulled at my hips and dragged me closer, gripping me hard and thrusting as long and fast as he could, driving in and out from the very tip of his lovely long sex all the way to his firm hard stomach and back until I thought it might slip out, but it was back inside, thrilling me again and again.

"You're a little pumpkin! Ahhh!" he sighed with pleasure, pulling me right down onto the stiffened sword. "You love it! You little bugger! You love it!"

"If you're happy, Eddie."

"Say you like it, Jackie! Tell me you like it!" he demanded.

"Yes! Yes! You know I do. I love it!" He just stopped dead. Speared to his firm brown belly, I felt him tremble. It was all over! I knew it, but Eddie kept saying, "It's going to happen any second. Something's going to happen! It will be too late!"

"Let it happen," I whispered. "Just let it happen and kiss me."

It felt as if he were part of me; every tiny vein and contour: the shape, heat, size and magic of his sex was part of me. I knew that I belonged to him and knew the shooting liquids in my body belonged to both of us. He just filled me with happiness and then broke down in tears.

"Forgive! Forgive!" he stuttered tearfully.

"Sh! Sh!" I took the gentle giant, kissed his damp hair and comforted him. "There's nothing to forgive, Eddie. I asked you. I made you! I can't help loving you and wanting you. Stop crying and cheer up!"

We walked naked to the bathroom, hand in hand like a man and his boy. It was delightful! We bathed, kissed, stroked and sploshed about like two friendly kids. Eddie sploshed his shaving cream all over my belly and put some on the tip of my nose.

He smelled fresh and fragrant when he'd finished. He made me fragrant, rubbing his lotion all over me, into my little bush, on my bottom and all over my back and shoulders. "You're gorgeous!" he said, picking me up in his big strong arms and carrying me into the room we shared.

My penis was still stiff, demanding and unsatisfied. Eddie stroked it lovingly. I knew he wanted it. He loved sucking boys and it thrilled me when he sucked at my magic wand. He had always called it an act of love, so I held his head gently and let him enjoy himself. When the sensations grew stronger, I began to drive it in and out, something I had not done before but in the past he'd never drawn anything from me. For just one moment I thought I should take it out and save him from the squirting seminal fluid, but then I thought perhaps he'd like it and drove it right home and let it throb on his tongue. The shooting stars shot from me and he tasted my love for the first time. It felt like magic. He had some of me in him and I had something from his lovely body in mine. We fell asleep with our lips touching, arms clasped and love flowing over our bodies like water.

Bright sunlight streamed through the open window and the scent of fresh garden flowers filled the room. Birds sang sweetly in the tree tops, and a passing milkman whistled a tune as he made his way along the tree-lined street, placing a bottle at someone's doorstep, picking up the empties and rattling them in the wire basket, pulling his handcart behind him, and breaking into song. "Milkeee-oooh!. . . Milkyo!"

Eddie turned to me and smiled. "Hi there!" he said, running the backs of his fingers along my cheek. "Did you sleep okay?"

"Lovely!" I replied. "Put your arm around me, Eddie."

"Are you happy, little one?" he whispered, cuddling me into his chest. "Do you like sleeping with me?"

"Very much," I answered. "Tell me, Eddie – do I act girlish?"

"Of course not!" he replied. "You're just a lovely handsome boy!"

"But I want a kiss," I said, quite concerned. "Surely that's being feminine?"

"You've got nothing to worry about," said Eddie, kissing the tip of my nose. "Your life will be full of kisses. You're a fine boy. Just a bit different that's all. There's millions of kids like you." He slipped out of bed with the most magnificent erection I had ever seen. I just had to make a grab at it.

"Don't get up!" I pleaded. "Let's have another hour in bed."

The springy penis reached right up past his navel and banged against his rippling stomach muscles as he bent to pick my discarded knickers from the floor. "Don't worry," said my man. "I'm just going for a pee. I'll be back in a minute."

It didn't take him long to wash and shave. His teeth gleamed and his lovely breath was fragrant in my mouth. He pulled the covers from us. "You know that you are a complete homosexual," he whispered, putting his forefinger on my boyish nipple, running it slowly across to the other one and then down my belly to touch the tip of my stiff little pigeon.

"What's that?" I asked innocently. "What is a homosexual?"

"A boy who likes having sex with other boys," replied Eddie. "Haven't you heard the word before?"

"No," said I, stroking his pole. "Anyway, sex doesn't interest me. I think I like being kissed more than anything else. The sexy bits just seem to make it nicer, but the kissing and loving is what I really like."

Eddie touched my forehead with his lips. "Then you're a homosexual," he said nice and friendly. "You don't go out with girls, do you?"

"Of course not!" I replied sharply. "I can't stand the things."

"You do like big strong men like me?" asked the lovely guy.

"Please stop talking about things like that," I said shyly. "You make me feel silly. I haven't been with any men. Just cuddle me and stop talking." Eddie picked me up and sat me on his nice brown belly looking into my eyes. "Tell me about the people you've had sex with?" he asked. "Don't be shy."

"I've been sleeping and bumming with my friend Eggy for a couple of years," I said, blushing and then getting into my stride when I saw his understanding smile. "We've made love lying down on the floor, kneeling down, standing up in the nude at the swimming pool and lots of ways, but we've not been with any men."

"You haven't sucked him? Have you?" asked Eddie, lifting me up and sitting me carefully on the great stiff spear.

"We tried," I replied, settling myself comfortably on the tip of his dickie. "But we couldn't go through with it. We've done this before."

"Let's get into the bath tub. I'm sure we could use a wash." So we started fooling around in the tub.

"Tell me more about your boyfriend," asked Eddie, throwing the wet sponge at my face. "He must be a very nice kid if you care for him so much. Is he as lovely as you?"

"Eggy is very handsome," I replied, putting my big toe up Eddie's bottom and giggling at his surprised look. "He is much better looking than me and he has lovely soft hair. We've been close ever since I can remember."

"Take you toe away," asked Eddie, "or I'll do the same to you but not with my toe! Tell me more about Eggy."

"There's nothing to tell," I replied, flipping his big dickie with the other foot. "I've told you all I can."

"I suppose he's a trustworthy lad," said Eddie, getting a bit inquisitive.

"I'd trust him with my life," I replied. "He's the most wonderful boy in the world, but I wouldn't trust him with you!"

"Bring your friend around any time," Eddie said, drying my bottom with a nice fluffy towel. "I like a boy about the house and he sounds like a good companion for you while I'm out late."

I promised that I would bring him round, but I was lying.

We had a happy day together, spending the early part of the evening playing chess and doing the crossword in the *Daily Herald*, Eddie's favourite newspaper. He liked it because he collected the coupons from the pages and I'm sure I liked it simply because of the crossword puzzle; it sent me searching through the dictionary and added a few more words to my ever-increasing vocabulary.

At night we made love and he sucked at my magic wand but even when he begged me to take him in my mouth, I simply couldn't.

It went on all week. I had to adjust; sleep by day alongside my man, and stay awake all night, twiddling with the radio while he patrolled the city streets. It was wonderful: he would return to his boy and find fresh coffee, the morning paper, bacon and egg, and a neatly set breakfast table awaiting him.

We just needed each other, loved one another dearly and could not bear to be apart. Sitting on his knee in the evening, dressed only in my little white shirt, kissing, fondling, stroking my cheek against his warm bare chest filled me with pleasure. We could hardly tear ourselves from the settee to go to bed.

Eventually, after dodging around from my parents and making all kinds of excuses for staying out late or not coming home at nights, I spoke to Eggy about it. "Listen," I said quite seriously. "I have a man friend, a real man!"

Eggy gave me some bubblegum and it put me off for a second. I blew a great giant bubble and it burst all over my face.

"When are you going to introduce me to him?" asked Eggy. We were not exactly shrinking violets! We were hard, tough city kids from the slums.

"When Nelson gets his fuckin' eye back!" I retorted. "This guy is mine! I need him. Do you understand?"

"Sure I do," replied my friend. "I've got a man myself. He takes me everywhere. He's much older than you or me, and I think I prefer it that way. We make love in his car and sometimes I sleep at his house, so I know how you feel."

"I'm going to tell my mother that I sleep at your place every weekend," I said. "Will you come home with me and convince her?"

We were sitting in his ma's living-room at the time. Eggy put his arm around my shoulder. "Sure I will," he said softly. "I'll do anything for you, Jackie." We kissed each other like gentle boys, soft and light like the touch of a butterfly wing.

"Will you still be my friend?" I asked him quietly. "This wouldn't make any difference, would it?"

"How could anything come between us?" asked Eggy. "Talk sense! We'll always be together. We'll see each other at school each day. I'll have my man at night and you'll be happy with your friend."

My mother raised no objections; I believe she was glad to get rid of me. I practically moved in with Eddie from that day onwards, but there were times when it was impossible to be with him because of the unsocial hours he worked. I could let myself into his home, use the lovely bathroom, and change into the nice clothes he kept for me. Unfortunately, I would be at school while he was at home, and when I was free, he would be on duty until well after midnight. Weekends of course were absolute heaven, and so were the times when his off-duty spells coincided with my own free time.

He often asked me to bring my friend home for company rather than let me be alone, but he didn't understand. A young boy cannot just moon around in an empty house feeling lonely so I spent my time on the streets unless Eggy was available, but he was usually involved with his new lover who seemed to be a relative of some kind.

Henry Tarleton, another schoolfriend, had a fight with me: just a silly schoolboy fight that turned into a boxing match in the schoolyard. We shook hands like professionals and he took me to his home in a small side street in Low Hill. We were reading comics and doing all the silly things that boys do, when his uncle came in. I had seen his uncle, Nel Tarleton, on the movies, in all the newspapers and plastered all over the city on hoardings. This was my first meeting in the flesh, so to speak, and I was quite surprised at his appearance. "How could such a small slim guy like this be the greatest boxer in the world!" I thought.

Henry worshipped his world-famous uncle and I think everyone in Liverpool did too because he had started in the gutter and fought his way to riches and fame. His friends and companions were all great boxers. Henry and I would sit and listen to them talk and they taught us many things.

The great Dom Volante, another famous boxer, used to spar with us, teach us the tricks of the trade and try and get us to join the boys' boxing club but we did not fancy boxing as a way of life.

"A guy fights with his brains. . . not his body," said Nel. "Watch out for the opponent's tricks and try to out-think him. Speed and footwork will save you every time. Watch the guy's eyes for signals. It's an art. The art of self-defence." Nel never knocked a guy out in his whole ring career, and yet he won all of his fights and fought long after all his contemporaries had retired.

I listened spellbound every evening. . . "If you have an injured right arm," said Ernie Roderick, "then you must try and convince the other guy that you have an injured left arm. A boxer with a bandage on his left knee is probably weak from an injury on the other knee, and if he smiles at you – that means you have hurt him badly. If you wanna do something against the rules. . . make sure your back is to the referee." It just went on and on until I thought that I could never believe anything any more.

However, my interest in boxing pleased my friend Eddie, so he bought some equipment and stepped up my boxing lessons. We fought in his garden, in his basement and in the spare room where he put me through all kinds of strenuous exercises.

It was great fun and usually finished up with a naked wrestling match. The good times we enjoyed made it all seem so beautiful and romantic, but there was another part of my life that was not so beautiful. . . the times when I could not see Eddie for days on end and went into the city feeling blue.

CHAPTER EIGHT

Liverpool Blues

Liverpool, Liverpool, dirty old town. Every generation had left its dreadful smell. The slavers had lined the salt-house docks with sweat and blood, Tate and Lyle's sugar factory made an even worse stench, with bare-breasted female labour sweating at the shovels, while the peanuts boiling down in Bibby's oil refinery made the' worst stink in dockland.

There were fourteen miles of dock road, and a brown double line of horse shit stretched from Bootle to far away Garston. Foul and stinking hovels lined the evil-smelling, steep streets which spread out in a fan shape until they reached the suburbs, where they called you posh if the kids wore shoes.

Protestants lived on the south side; Catholics lived on the north side – Scotland Road, Phoebe Anne Street and a street so foul with the stench of boiling cabbage, pig's feet, bones and tails that I was afraid to venture into the place: William Henry Street with its doss houses, fourpence a bed.

"*Echo* koshers" were guys who sold the *Echo*, Liverpool's own newspaper. They grabbed an armful of *Echo*'s under one skinny arm and ran barefoot through the city streets and as far out into the suburbs as their rasping lungs would take them, shouting as they went, "Last City *Echo*! Last City *Echo*!"

They frightened me. I was afraid of the *Echo* koshers because they looked like sick consumptive skeletons and I didn't want to catch their dreadful disease. When they spat on the pavement, and this they did continually, streams of red-spattered blood came from their thin-lipped mouths to land on the pavement's edge. This caused the tramway corporation to set up notices at the stops: "No Spitting!"; the tram stops were a favourite place for the koshers.

Evil-smelling Mary Ellens sold fruit, fish, vegetables and beautiful bunches of sweet smelling violets from their barrows.

The staple breakfast diet was: nothing on Monday, bugger all on Tuesday, Sweet F.A. for the rest of the week and "Salt fish" on Sunday. Salt fish! They sang about it! "Oh give me Sunday morning and the old salt fish, 'cos I've got the Liverpool blues!"

Salt fish was like a piece of stiff white leather, covered in rock salt, and if you put it in a bucket on Saturday night, then it absorbed all the moisture and became a fish for Sunday breakfast.

The bucket should have been full of fresh water, but as most families only had one bucket I fear the water was not too fresh.

Salt water men – sailors from all over the world – roamed the city streets: Lascars, Chinamen, Arabs, Indians, Coolies – half naked and straight from the scuppers of Singapore, Yanks, Polacks, and husky looking, blond Norwegians.

Liverpool was one of the richest cities in the world, and nobody had a job. The Arthur Scargill of the day was a guy named Leo McRae, and I saw him get his head smashed in many a time by the cops before they slung him in the Bridewell. His boss, a guy named Oswald Moseley who fared a little better than the rabble-rousing Leo, dressed his followers in black shirts, had an armed bodyguard, screamed out for equal rights and wanted to change the world.

It wasn't a nice world for a sensitive and gentle homosexual boy of thirteen. I wanted no part of it, ran from the dreadful world of reality and created a world of my own: a fantasy world in the cinema seats where I dreamed of lovely clothes, beautiful young men, expensive hotels, gangsters in snow-white dinner jackets, gorgeous black bow-ties and sleek, chromium-plated automobiles with long black shiny bonnets.

It is true that I loved Eddie dearly, but boys and young men simply fascinated me and I found myself searching for members of my own sex: a third sex that nobody spoke about and, I fear, very few understood. To see a handsome young man out on the town with his boy was a delight to my eyes. I recognised them instantly. It tore at my heart strings and made me wish that Eddie had a different job and could take me out like that.

Getting into the cinema became more difficult for me; a local bye-law demanded that youngsters must be accompanied by a parent or adult. I wore short trousers as all boys did until they left school. The kids would laugh at a boy in long trousers: "Help! Where's the fire?" "Where did you get the longees?" "Look. . . Fuckin' 'ell! 'e's gorri's dad's kecks on!"

Consequently, young boys wishing to enter a cinema would stand outside, watch for a reasonably friendly face and, almost poking the stranger's eye out with the proffered admission money, say, "Take us in, mister!" It only took about ten minutes or so, one or two rejections, and then the kid would strike lucky: the stranger would take the cash, buy two tickets and have to sit with the kid during the performance.

Eggy and I were experts at spotting the right kind of people and never failed to get in to a show. I could have taken us in through the exit doors, but my friend was a good boy and wouldn't do anything like that.

When I was alone, however, I felt rather shy about approaching strangers. I would stand like a fool and let people pass while other boys importuned successfully. My targets were usually a small family group, or man and wife. Single men touched you up, felt your bum and asked for a little favour. Young lovers didn't wish to be disturbed so they were out.

Standing outside the Majestic Cinema one day, money clutched in my fist and eyes alert for the right person, I spotted a happy-looking young man and his schoolboy son. The boy was skipping, his arm linked to that of his dad, clinging on and obviously going to enter the Majestic. It looked just right for me. When they reached the bright lights, I shoved my cash into the guy's face and said, "Will you take me in please?"

"Jackie!" said the boy.

"Hi, Eggy. I didn't recognise you."

"My schoolfriend," said Eggy, introducing me. The man was very friendly, considerate, handsome and obviously my chum's special friend. He took the cash from me and we went into the cinema. I knew Eggy was very happy with the guy. The love light in his eyes told me that much. This made me quite happy and hope that they had as great a love for each other as I had for my man.

During the interval, the guy bought three ice creams, refused my cash and settled down comfortably with his boy. A blonde old bag walked up and down the aisles, spraying a perfumed disinfectant all over the audience. It contained some chemical which the health authorities thought useful in the battle against TB, a dreaded incurable disease of the times.

Another short-skirted blonde walked the aisles shouting, "Cigarettes! Matches! Cigarettes! Matches! Ice cream! Chocolate! Cigarettes! Matches!" A guy played an illuminated organ adorned with artificial light and the audience sang along with him as the smoke from a thousand Woodbines curled up to the ceiling. It was great. . . if you had rubber lungs!

"Why are you looking so sad?" asked Eggy, leaning over to me. "I thought you would be with your friend."

"I can't see him for a week," I replied, leaning across the man's knees.

Good old Eggy touched my hand. "Are you lonely?"

"Just a bit," I answered casually.

"You can come home with us if you wish," said my friend, smiling at me.

"Three's a crowd. . . I'd be in the way," I said.

"You're quite welcome," said the young man. "I know how close you are. Timmy talks about you all the time."

Timmy. . . the name sounded strange. Eggy was much better. He'd go potty if I called him Tim at school

"Don't spend the weekend by yourself, Jackie. Stay with us." Eggy linked arms with his friend as the lights went down. "Please, Jack, I don't like seeing you all alone," he whispered in the dimming light.

The next time the lights came on, every member of the audience stood up, remained perfectly still and sang the National Anthem to the music from the beautiful organ. Then there was a rush for the exits. On the way out, you could hear the doorman shouting at the top of his voice, "Fourpence, fivepence and sixpenny seats only!"

The smell of fish and chips filled our nostrils. The man linked my arms to his and Eggy's and we skipped along like happy children. A "Green Goddess" – the most magnificent, chromium-plated, dazzlingly modern tramcar ever designed – slid silently to a halt at the stop and, starry-eyed, we jumped on the super spacecraft in case it vanished before our very eyes.

The world was changing fast! The sound of an aircraft overhead would bring people to a dead stop. They would point up into the bright blue sky and shout, "Look! There's an airy!" A guy named Hore-Belisha filled the country with yellow beacons. They said he was going to do away with the cavalry next and replace the horse with armoured cars. People laughed at that one and made jokes about his yellow balls.

"How about some fish and chips, boys?"

"Yummy!" We picked up our supper, wrapped in the Last City *Echo*, and skipped up the garden path to Eggy's weekend paradise. Inside it was warm and cosy. Fish and chip papers went onto the roaring coal fire and we sat together, the man in his armchair, the Egg and I holding hands on the settee.

"You make a lovely pair!" He stroked our pink cheeks. Eggy slid to his knees, put his lips to his friend's rising dickie, and his gentle hands round his waist. He loved the man. The bulging trousers told me so.

"Is it alright if Jackie sleeps in our bed?" asked Eggy.

"If that's what you want, Tim," replied his friendly man.

"I just want you," said Timmy, "but I don't want Jackie to sleep alone."

"I can sleep anywhere," I said. "I don't want to disturb you."

"You won't disturb us," said the young man. "Get undressed and hop into bed. Go with him, Tim. I'll be there later."

Eggy undressed and slipped into bed naked. "Take your knickers off, Jackie. Sleep in the nude like me," he said, waving his dickie.

"What about your friend?"

"Paul? He loves me. I love him like mad! I'd do anything for him. I do. . . I do anything he wants. I won't be jealous if he plays with you. I know he loves boys."

"I've got a man, Eggy. I'm in love!" I said quite seriously.

"You're lonely. . . Take your knickers off and I'll give you a cuddle." We were always happy together; warm smooth bellies and fencing pigeons, pink-cheeked faces and sweet red lips; just happy and comfy. My hair was all mixed up and mingled with that of my chum, spread out on the pillow like two heads of hair in one.

"Where do I sleep?" said Eggy's brown and naked lover.

"In the middle!" we shouted.

We lay, all three holding hands for a few minutes, my young friend's head on his lover's chest. Paul stroked Eggy's soft dark hair for a second or two, and the boy took the big man's dickie in between his lips and sucked it right in front of me. It made me excited. I started pulling my wire, as the kids called it. Eggy stopped his oral caresses. "You're not lonely now are you, Jackie?" he enquired, licking his lips with pleasure.

"You're a lovely friend," I whispered. "I'm very happy with you." Paul kissed me tenderly and put the lights out. I don't know what they were doing but I know what I was doing. Eggy suddenly laughed out loud. Paul took my hand and stopped me from playing with myself.

"Put the lights on, Paul," said Eggy. "I will if Jackie is willing."

The lights went on. Eggy climbed across his friend and lay on my belly. "Stop playing with your pigeon, Jackie. Paul wants to see us bumming each other. What do you say?"

"It's better than pulling my wire," said I, getting up from the big warm bed.

How does one describe an act of love between two gentle thirteen year old boys who have been in love with each other since their first joint erection? It is too beautiful to describe.

Paul, the eye-witness, standing over us, legs apart, brown-skinned body, golden-haired testicles swinging in the light cast by the electric standard lamp, strange piercing blue eyes gleaming, powerful bronzed chest muscles shiny with body heat, strong muscular back, showing every delightful contour of his masculine strength and power, gorgeous thick golden hair loose upon his manly, handsome forehead, engorged dickie shiny with moist heat as he stroked it gently. . . he could have described it.

He must have seen Eggy's youthful erection enter his lover, seen the brightness and love in the boys' eyes, the sweet dainty triangles of youthful puberty, the swift movements, flashing little pale bottoms almost white against the youngsters' sun-bronzed backs and legs, the sweet little pink openings, ripe red lips that kissed, pink tongues that showed through slightly open mouths, teeth that shone like ivory castles. . . He must have heard the boyish giggles as the driving young tiger reached the point of no return, shuddered with pleasure as the stiff young pigeon shot the milky fluid and filled the loved one.

And what of the return match? What happened when it was all over and the spent boys knelt gasping on the carpet of the warm bedroom floor?

"I suppose you want to bum the pair of us now?"

"I do," said Paul, advancing with eight-inch sword in hand. "Who's first?"

"ME!" we shouted.

It was a very happy, carefree night. Filled to the brim with sweet love, we were all far too exhausted to even cover our bodies and fell into a dreamless sleep naked upon the big warm bed.

Paul, being the good host he was, made us jump into the tub while he prepared our breakfast. It was wonderful!

"Has your man friend sucked your dick?" enquired my horny chum.

"Hundreds of times," I replied. "He loves it."

Eggy smiled. "Have you?"

"No. Never," I said. "I wanted to. I still do, but it worries me."

"I was a bit scared myself at first," said Eggy, "but I like it now. I love sucking Paul. Try it on Eddie. He'll love you for it."

"He loves me already," I said, ducking his curly head beneath the tap.

Paul bathed while we ate.

The weekend flew as if on wings. "Call any time, Jackie. We're always together. You boys can sit, kiss and cuddle while you're in my home. It was a pleasure, just seeing you so close," were his parting words.

We did just that, just being boys, while Paul read his paper and got on with his daily life.

Eddie was different. He was just my Eddie. I loved him. Eggy – the love we shared was indescribable. Sitting at his side in school, sharing our sexy little secrets, sometimes puzzled at our own strange feelings. One part of my chemical content drew me to him, strong and masculine for the beauty and youth he had; the laughing boy made me feel strong and manly, even lustful. . . alive! The other half of me drew me to Eddie. . . My man! I was feminine and wanted him to love me, take me, be inside my body! It was all too much for my childish mind to cope with.

I'd been involved in so much dickie licking lately that I decided to go all the way with Eddie – do everything he wanted and just love him to death. I mentioned it to Eggy. "Eddie's got a whole week off. I'm going to suck it for him, love him silly and not get out of bed all week."

"You'll like it, Jackie. It's better than bumming. I love it!"

"Eggy?"

"Yeah!"

"Strange . . . strange you and I haven't sucked each other."

"Do you want to?"

"No. . . I just want Eddie. I love you like hell! Understand?"

Holding hands in the shadows, rough kids from St Jude's. . .

Eddie was waiting patiently. "Take a shower, Jackie. Put something nice on and wear a good overcoat. I'm taking you out tonight," he said impatiently.

"Will you link arms with me, Eddie?"

"Yes dear," he replied in a fatherly voice.

"Promise!"

"Honestly! Hurry along – we're having a chicken dinner in town. Get dressed, monkey – we'll be late for the theatre."

Special treat – I've got a special treat for you tonight! thought I.

Boys linked to men just fascinated me. Linking arms probably gave me more satisfaction than making love. It has always been accepted in Liverpool. The only place I've seen happy young boys linking arms with men is Blackpool – funny 'ats, links of happy drunks spread across the pavement and lovely boys linked up with their friends.

I recognized boys like myself instantly, gave a friendly wink and sometimes made a date. Handsome boys, obviously from my own background by their speech, manners and general behaviour, accompanied by a man from a different walk in life – different social strata and still willing to openly defy the class barrier and all its taboos – sent shivers of delight up my spine. Instantly, and without even knowing anything about the daring couple, I simply loved them.

However, I also knew of a certain boy who was given a simple after-school job with a wealthy ship's chandler, moved into the gentleman's home and became his business partner in the shipping industry before he was seventeen. He was very industrious, intelligent, and no doubt deserved his position. They were lovers nevertheless, wined and dined together and were accepted by the whole community.

The fascinating thing about this type of relationship was the very fact that it was accepted. Intelligent people must have known the love affair existed; such affairs have gone on for centuries. Ergo, society accepted and allowed a man his boy, but only if he could afford one. . . The only other conclusion one can reach is that the few people who realised such relationships existed were homosexual.

Fortunately, during my first year at school, it became possible for a child to be legally adopted. A man might give an unfortunate boy a helping hand and, if a relationship developed, approach the boy's parents and offer him a better chance in life: possibly a position in his household, and even an offer of adoption. Things were extremely hard for poor families, and the standard reply, if a boy or girl wished to move on, better him or herself or go into household service, the armed forces or the merchant navy was, "Go! We won't stand in your light."

Poor families got into debt, mostly through unemployment, drinking and absolute depression. Dole queues reached hundreds of yards and the depressed men in the queues were subject to verbal abuse from the business-suited and better-educated dole clerks. The next step in the horrifying situation was that the dole money ran out after a limited time and the family came under parish rules and regulations.

The parish supplied pink food vouchers instead of money, parish medicines for the sick, and the parish orphanage for the children of families thrown into the street for not paying the rent. The father went into the Salvation hostel until he found another place of abode for his family. God knows what happened to the mother but the kids went into the parish children's home.

"Mother, mother, take me home, from this hungry parish home," sang the snotty-nosed boys in care. The girls skipped in a rope and sang, "Daddy, Daddy, Uncle Jack, will you come and take me back? I've been here a week or two, and now I want to be with you. Me clothes are torn, me shoes are bent, mother couldn't pay the rent. Daddy went and got the sack, so they put me in a home with me ears pinned back. . ." I spent years worrying about having my ears pinned back and wondered how it would be done.

Anybody seeing me linked up with Eddie would assume I was his nephew, young brother or possibly his son. He didn't seem to mind anyway. We tripped along to the tram stop, hopped aboard a moving Green Goddess and sped silently into town. Young, agile people always boarded and skipped off the trams whilst they were on the move. It seemed the norm. The local term was "skipping on" or "skipping off". We skipped off at the chicken house, while the fabulous Green Goddess went on to the Pier Head to be sullied by the screaming gulls.

"We didn't link arms in town," I complained.

"Eat your chicken. We can link arms on the way to the theatre."

"It's lovely."

"The chicken?"

"Linkin' arms, silly!"

"How's the chicken?" asked Eddie, touching my knee under the table.

"Wonderful! I've got a wishbone. Will you make a wish with me?"

I threw him my most friendly smile. "Pull the wishbone, Eddie. Make a lovely special wish for you and me. I know your wish will come true tonight."

He pulled the wishbone and he got the biggest piece.

"Just wish, Eddie. Wish for anything you want from me tonight and your wish will come true," I said with a smile on my happy face.

"I bet it won't – it never does," remarked my friend dryly.

"Give me your arm? Now let's go! The Shakespeare next stop!"

"Wow! The Shakespeare!" We skipped along arm in arm to Shakespeare Street. I felt quite posh when the cloakroom attendant took our hats and coats, and like a young prince when we were shown into the deep red plush of the finest seats.

No fussy blonde old bags, no peanut shells beneath our warm clad feet, no screaming dolls shouting out their wares, no cigarette smoke in the fresh clean air, no crying kids, no Mary Ellens at the pavement edge. . .

The Shakespeare: Mmmm! The painted faces of the performers met us at the highly polished brass-railed bar. They drank with the audience, seated or standing around the elegant saloon, smiled at me, winked at me and made gorgeous theatrical jokes.

The show? I hardly noticed it! The Shakespeare – I noticed that. I smelt it, felt it, sat in it and absorbed the wonderful atmosphere of my first night at the theatre. . .

Clapping hands! Clapping hands! And clapping hands again until they tingled and the artist came back, thanked the delightful audience and gave an encore. Real live artists!

A well-dressed gentleman helped me into my coat – his name was Eddie. I loved him. "Let's walk all the way home, Eddie."

"It's cold, Jackie."

"I don't care. I want to walk home. Will you walk?"

He linked my arm and I tingled all over.

"It's only a mile, Eddie."

"You're a funny kid," he whispered in my cold ear.

"You're a handsome man," I replied

"I can't wait to get you home," said Eddie.

"And me! Let's walk faster."

A cold wind blew up from the Mersey, raised the crumpled *Echo*'s and discarded tram tickets from the filthy streets and sent them rustling along the pale flagged pavements like a ticker-tape cascade, catching round our legs.

The Pip! Pip! Pip! of the tug-boats. . . Booming fog-horns over the murky waters. . . Gulls in the night sky. . . Smells of Irish stew and hot scouse in the mean streets we pass. . . Horses' hooves clattering on the square, old-fashioned highway. . . Gleaming, steel lines of tramways as far as the eye can see. . . "Taxi!" shouted a drunken sailor. . . A match flickered in a darkened doorway as we passed a courting couple, or some painted whore with a fine seafaring lad.

My legs were cold but the wind didn't care. It carried on and on, smashing against the crumbled sooty brickwork of the Church Of The Sacred Heart and sending the filthy cinders in our faces.

Eddie stopped. "Are you alright, son? Are you cold?"

"No. I'm fine." He pulled my overcoat collar up, settled my school cap on my head and kissed the tip of my nose. "Cherry nose – your nose is freezing!"

"I'm nice and warm, Eddie. It's a lovely coat."

It was lovely! Nice thick sturdy shoes, warm woollen stockings, a school cap! God! If my mates saw me in a school cap, they'd stick it down the shit-house!

A rattling old tramcar, the ale-house smell. . . Reminding me of my dad – bastard!. . . Pigs' feet, boiling cabbage, a smell of vinegared chips.

"Do you want something to eat, son?"

"I'm full of roast chicken and banana split."

"Almost home!"

"Unlink me, Eddie." I ran up the garden path, key in hand. . .

Eddie throws his smart expensive hat like a movie actor and laughs in suprise as it lands on the hatrack in the vestibule.

"Coffee, son? Hot milk?"

"Nothing. . . Straight to bed."

"Up you go then. Jackie!"

"Yes?"

"Keep your little white shirt on. I like to see you in a shirt."

He lets me undress him, and I keep my little white shirt on to please the handsome man. Only his nice little shorts remain. Then I kneel before him in my shirt tails. . .

"Do you like me, Eddie? I haven't really got a cherry nose,

have I?" Fingers hook into his knickers, lips press against the rising sex, shorts off, young mouth open wide. Fingers in my hair. "Do it, Eddie! Put it in my mouth. I want you to."

"Have you done it to someone? I thought you didn't really want to do this?"

"I want you to put it in my mouth, Eddie! No one else, no one!"

"I'll come in your mouth, dear. I'll have to!"

"Do it! That's what I want."

"Take it in your hand, son, and put it in yourself."

"Do it, Eddie. You put it in. That's what I want – that's exactly what I want."

"You look so beautiful in your little white shirt tails, sucking me. Just suck the end gently. . ."

I hardly moved. The beautiful thing began to move in and out. My man was in my mouth. He tasted of my man, my lovely Eddie, bouncing against the roof of my soft mouth, striking the lips, sweet secretions flowing gently on my tongue, pulsating veins in my lips, golden hair before my eyes.

"Suck it, darling! Suck it hard! Now suck it gently, tickle it with your little pink tongue. . . Thank you darling!"

He's never called me darling before! What will the shooting liquid taste like? Shall I spit it out or drink it down like he does? So wonderful to please him so. . .

"Pinch my bottom gently if you want the love seeds in your mouth. . . I'm almost finished. . ."

I pinch his bottom gently. How can I show him that I wish to drink it down? The giant penis fills my mouth with ecstacy. The seed shoots into my mouth, over my tongue. The taste is Eddie – Eddie, honey and sweet white wine!

"Darling! Darling!. . . DARLING BOY!!!"

He loves me now. I drink it down. . . Will he kiss me, taste his beautiful taste on my tongue, share the sperm on my lips, in my mouth? One tiny drop remains on the tip of his shining wand and I take it on the tip of my tongue and keep it for my lover to share with me, one sparkling jewel. "Love you, sweetheart boy. Love you, love you, love you. . ."

Eddie slips the white shirt from me, carries me and places me naked on his bed. "I love you, Jackie. You are the most delightful young boy in the world." We kiss and share the tiny jewel I saved.

"You know I love you now, Eddie. We both have your taste on our tongue. You're sweet and wonderful. I'll do anything for you now. Every night. Every day. Kiss you all over. Suck at your nipples, your beautiful dickie, anything you want. I just love you."

"I know," he whispered. "I know now. . .."

"Kiss me again. It was heavenly!"

Eddie kisses me. "Why? Why, Jackie? Why?"

"Because it pleased you. I'm sorry I waited so long. It gave me pleasure too. I really love you with all my heart."

He kisses my nose. "It's not a cherry nose, darling. It's a very handsome nose. I was only teasing. You are very handsome, masculine, pretty, gorgeous, everything in the world."

"Get on your knees, Eddie. I'm going mad to kiss the golden hairs on your bum," I cry excitedly.

"What's come over you?"

"I'm just growing up. I've learned a lot from my schoolfriend lately, the boy I've been in love with all my life."

"Did you suck him?" asked my handsome man.

"No. You're the only one. You know it's true. I tell you everything. Eggy, my friend, he has a man – it's just like you and me. They're in love and Eggy sucks his friend like you suck me. . . You must know that you would be the first. You must!"

"I know. I know, Jackie."

"You know I sleep with Eggy sometimes. I told you we had sex together. You are the only man. I just want to be your boy, because I love you. Now get on your knees and let me kiss your golden hair before you fall asleep."

He gets on his knees. My nose touches his little pink sensitive spot as I kiss the soft downy hairs on his lovely, swinging sack of silken skin. The sack, heavy with his weighty masculinity, swings away from my lips and I watch fascinated as it swings toward my lips again. Each time I kiss the swinging sack of weighted beauty, my nose, my thirteen year old nose which turned cherry red in the wind, touches his virgin, manly opening.

Every time this happens, Eddie whispers the word I love so much: "Darling". I like to hear him say "darling" so I keep kissing the swinging object of desire. It hypnotises me. My little nose, however, is not giving him enough satisfaction, so I substitute my tongue. Again the pointed tongue penetrates, and yet again. "Darling! Darling boy!" he cries in ecstacy.

"Eddie!"

"Darling boy!"

"I want to swear!"

"Swear, you silly boy."

"Let me fuck you!"

"Fuck me, Jackie! Fuck me! No one has ever fucked me. I want it to be you."

"You like my magic wand?" I enquire, as if I didn't know.

"I love it. . . Fuck me hard. . . Harder!"

"It's going to be a wonderful week, you lovely big man. You're the first man I've bummed. Keep still. . . Wow! It's. . . I think it's coming. . . Eddie. . . Eddie. . ."

I pump away, stronger than I've ever known before. Thoughts flash through my mind: thoughts, thrills, thoughts. . . We've never used swear words – why now? What strange chemistry in my silly body is at work? What made him call me darling? He usually calls me pumpkin or something daft like that. What is it that changes me from girl to boy in a flash? "Eddie! It's too late! It's wonderful!"

We cuddle down together. "Sorry about the swearing."

"I used a few silly words myself," replies my man, satisfied at last.

It was the first time for many things tonight: the lovely skipping, linked up with my man, the shooting stars on my tongue, and now this! God almighty! Eddie. . . Eddie speared to my magic wand like a. . . like a what. . .? A homosexual? Not Eddie, not my big strong Eddie. He's my man and I'm his boy, his beautiful boy!

"I'm sorry about everything, Eddie." I whisper quietly.

"Shush! Give me your hand – let's go asleep holding hands."

I just moved in with him after that: his house was mine. I was his boy, he was my man: we didn't need anybody else.

I managed to get a good part-time job in "Paddy's Market". The stall owner was a Mary Ellen. She had two pretty daughters, a handsome young son and a heart of pure gold. The money was good. She gave me clothes from her stall and offered me a bed in her home. My family didn't want me anyway. Nor did they care where I slept. They had some idea of my whereabouts – knew I had a home with Eggy or the market trader and kept pestering me for beer money, even though I was still a schoolboy.

While they were sleeping off their drunkenness, I was working, earning and singing my head off at six o'clock in the mornings, laughing at life and happy all day long. At night, when the cold winds came up from the river and the drunks, whores and homeless paper boys shivered in the streets, I was warm and cosy – snuggled up with my Eddie.

We just lived and loved, gave each other as much as was demanded by the loving relationship that held us together and grew stronger with each passing day. I was dying to leave school, get a full-time job to earn more cash and try to pay Eddie back for his kind deeds, the home he'd given me and, most of all, for taking me off the streets.

CHAPTER NINE

A Walk in the City

School's out! No more school! I could hardly believe it. I could wear long trousers and nobody would laugh at me.

The city called! "Fuck Paddy's Market!" I said to myself. "There'll be a job in the city for a kid like me. If there ain't, then I'll find another friggin' city."

The whole week to myself! It seemed strange. Smells! The city drew me to its evil-smelling bosom. Brunswick Road – the first step into the new world. I knew I would succeed. Past the German pork butcher shop. The smell of steaming hot pork pies, fresh out of the oven. Black puddings being tied in crazy horseshoe shapes: the string of bloody sausage dangling, the black and blood-stained lips of the cook as he tied the pudding in links with a string, pudding string in mouth, fingers moving like those of a skilled pianist, links getting longer and longer until they dangled in the sawdust-covered floor. The blood-stained cook winked at me, hung the black puddings in the window and winked at me again. Salt beef in great enormous barrels. Fresh and steaming hams, hot water dripping from the luscious gammons. Pressed beef, pressed pork and golden-crumbed hocks. Savoury tomato sausage, all pink and smelling spicy. Faggots! Steaming faggots made from a mix of animal lung and spices, veined shiny skin from the intestines of the pig bind the faggots tight and tempting. I winked back at the dirty-aproned cook and moved on down the road.

Tichbourne Terrace! Who the hell was Tichbourne to have such an evil-smelling dwelling named after him? I held my nose and passed a crocodile of white-haired children, all blind – stone blind albino childen from the basket-weaving blind school down the road. They frightened me, these beautiful white-haired, pink-eyed orphans. What made them blind? Some terrible disease?

"Fine ripe American apples!"

"Salt fish! Salt fish! Fresh Finney 'addock!" a stinking Mary Ellen cried.

Boys washed the windows of the shops in London Road. The pawnshop's golden balls gleamed in the morning sun. An ancient, bearded Jewish man rubbed his palms, removed the shutter from his pawnshop window and awaited the bundles. "Mary Ellen at the pawnshop door, a bundle in her hand an' a bundle on the floor," I whistled the happy tune. "I asked for 'alf a crown an' I stamped upon the floor, then I knocked the fuckin' bollocks off the pawnshop door."

A beautiful post-office boy rode past on a scarlet bicycle. He looked delightful in his neat little pill-box hat, so I winked at him and he smiled. Ah! The freedom of my first day! Young men brushed last night's spit-stained sawdust from the ale-house floors, gathered it in heaps and pushed it into the dirt-filled gutter.

"Two-a-penny lemons!"

"Salt! Block salt!" shouted a man, flat-capped and white rimed. "Block salt! Salt a penny a block!"

Steel-shod hooves dug into the cobbles to give the straining steeds a purchase as they heaved the steel-rimmed wagon wheels up the hill. A traction engine, coal-fired and spitting steam, a sweating, filthy stoker at the shovel and blue-capped driver at the ancient wheel. . . How strange the silent, sleek Green Goddess among this lumbering dockland traffic! A smell of brown sugar and molasses, black treacle and syrup in my nose from the smoking factory chimney on the skyline. No more school!

The new tunnel beneath the Mersey, all white and dusty from the chipping of the stone-masons, looked strange and out of place. A giant shadow from the Higson's brewery chimney, almost like a finger pointing to the sky, reached out to cover the small red globe that is the sun. The smell of French polish from the furniture factory, and the dust in my nose from the carpenters at their work.

"Ah! The city smells. . . but wait – what's this? Some golden-haired young beauty, ink-stained fingers, bright blue eyes: an office boy. Can I catch the angel's sparkling eye? He looks a peach, piled up with envelopes for the morning post.

I follow him, gaze longingly at his lovely shape, watch him as he stuffs the pillar box and follow him back to his office. No luck!

Sweet freedom! I'll find a beauty yet – I must – my first day on the loose. The strange feeling of freedom has made me horny for a boy. Would Eddie understand?

The sign reads: T.J. Hughes, Men's and Boy's Outfitter. Perhaps I should look at their display. I gaze wistfully, full of thought. Shall I go inside? Should I try on a pair of long trousers for the first time in my life?

Three scruffy-looking *Echo* koshers stumble bleary-eyed down the cold stone steps of the Salvation Army Men's and Boys' Hostel. I shudder. I could have turned out like these poor bastards if it hadn't been for the kindness that Eddie showered upon me. Long trousers! I'll go inside.

"What can I do for you, young man?"

"I'd like a pair of long trousers please."

"Have you just left school?"

"Yes."

"Let me look at you? Hmmmnnn! I should say about a twenty-six waist. Yes. I'll have to measure your leg."

"I'd like the grey flannel."

He puts the tape measure to my leg, reaches right up into my shorts, touches my dickie with the back of his hand and smiles at me.

"Well! You are a big lad! Go into the changing-room and take off your shorts." The young man showed me to the little curtained alcove. "I'll be with you in a minute." He comes back a few seconds later. "Are you shy?"

"Not really."

"Well, take your trousers off!"

Unfortunately the whole idea of removing my trousers in front of him has made me horny. I stand there like a fool.

"Let me help you," he says, removing my shorts. They slipped off quite easily.

"Try these," he says. I slip into the grey flannels and he helps me button the fly.

"I think they are just a bit too long, don't you?"

"Looks like it."

"Slip them off." My tight little knickers cannot hide the stiffened dickie. "What do you think about some underwear to go with the trousers? We have a nice selection of boys' undershorts. Would you like me to fetch you a pair?"

I blush. "The trousers will be enough for me. I might not even buy them."

He seems nice enough, but I want a boy. I have my own man. The moment his back is turned, I slip into my shorts and leave. A boy! A boy! I want a nice boy like myself!

Back once more on the city streets, the smell of frying onions is in my nostrils and the sense of freedom in my veins.

"Woolworth's," said the sign. "Woolworth's fivepence and sixpence store. Nothing over sixpence! Cafeteria upstairs! Take the moving staircase! Nothing over sixpence!"

The moving staircase draws me to its sliding maw. It's so simple that I could have invented it myself. But never in my wildest dreams could I have invented the gorgeous young creature who sits at my table. He's about my age: fourteen or fifteen, and wears the blue cap of the Liverpool Collegiate, a great college that had its own military unit – the kids went to school dressed like soldiers and carrying rifles on their fine young shoulders.

Our eyes meet. We know we're meant for each other. One of my own kind, at last!

"I'm going for another cup of tea," he says. "Would you like one?"

"Thank you. Here's the money," I reply.

"Don't be silly! It's only a penny!"

Talk is unnecessary. We can read each other's minds, think each other's thoughts, feel the desire for each other just as if it was written on a card about our necks.

When we use the men's room, see the wonderful effect and look into each other's eyes, we say, simultaneously:

"Where should we go?"

"Where can we go?" I whisper, fastening my trousers. "We can't do it here!"

"What do you want?" he says shyly, blushing, eyes bright with sparkling youth.

"You. I want you!"

"What's your name?"

"Jackie. What's yours?"

"Andrew. We can go into a hotel," he says, acting like a

grown-up man.

"That's foolish!" I reply.

"No, it's not. Come with me. I know what I'm doing." Sweet Andrew walks me to a hotel in the city, steps into the lift and says to the bell boy, "Third floor please." The youngster salutes, presses a button and deposits us on the third floor.

"Now what?"

"Don't worry, Jackie. My daddy has an office and a suite of rooms in this hotel," he says, taking my hand. "Come this way."

"I'm scared, Andrew. I just want you."

"I know you do. Let's go in one of the bathrooms."

Two seconds in the bathroom, two seconds for a kiss.

"Andrew, take your trousers off."

"Put some soap on my bottom, Jackie."

"We don't need it. I won't hurt you. I think you're lovely. Lean over the tub and open your legs very wide. I'm awful horny for you!"

"Dick me! Dick me, Jackie!"

"I'm right up you, Andy!" I hadn't heard the expression before.

"You're not dicking me!" says Andrew in his piping, boyish voice.

"Don't you like it?"

"Yes. I love it! But dick me – play with my dick. Make me spunk off!"

Sweet Andrew! I drove the stiffened sword deep in his lovely bum, dicked him with an experienced hand, shuddered with pleasure and heard the ping ping ping of his silver bullets on the tub-side.

"Andrew, you were great!"

"Do you often get in Woolworth's cafeteria?" says the boy.

"I will in future," I reply, fastening my trouser-front.

"I'll take my lunch there every day," he adds, smiling, washing and looking very happy.

"Do you really live in this lovely big hotel, Andrew?"

"No. It's my daddy's place of business. Come on – I'll be late for school."

Down the lift we go, past the dainty boy all pink and blue, silver buttoned, perky and diminutive, saucy little bum, nice, close-fitted uniform, a smile upon his face. Such a tiny boy!

Andrew flees! Once more I stroll the city streets, no longer horny for a friend, eyes alert, nostrils aware. The dusty road-sweeper leans upon his broom, horse shit at his booted feet, droppings everywhere.

Through the smoky railway-station yard into the station proper – great clouds of steam, piercing noises, a dozen clocks upon the wall, each with a different time. "Stephenson's Rocket" reads the sign. "Impossible," think I. But there it is, right before my very eyes, the famous locomotive: Liverpool and Manchester Railway 1830. No replica this!

A handsome sailor wishes to seduce me. I can see it in his eye and return his sweet suggestive wink, tail him to the men's lavatory and watch him flip his flap. No knickers 'neath the sailor's square cut fly, just a great long sexy organ. I look at it, longingly. Then I run away, laughing. Ah! The freedom of the city streets.

What else can I find to while away my day? I'm supposed to be seeking a job but it's all too interesting for such drudgery as that.

The tall ships at the busy dockside, great ocean-going liners, dumpy tug-boats, speedy police motorboats, an ancient square-rigger and a squatting bunch of lazy dockers playing cards with filthy pasteboards in their grimy hands. Great grey-green waves of salt sea water crash against the floating pier and lift it gently on its anchored chains.

"Join the Royal Marines!" shouts one sign. "No entry! One way only!" shouts another. I spy my first one-way street. Such nonsense! One way indeed! I know a dozen different ways, and a couple of entrances. . .

A crashing sound above my head and the rattle of the rails warns me of a fast approaching railway train on the overhead railway. Steam belching from its stumpy stack, it flashes by. Its journey? The seven-mile stretch of dockland to the north, dropping off the seamen and picking up the dockland workers at the stops.

The great city is alive with colour. The tall red chimney stack of Higson's brewery. Gleaming harness on the sweating animals, white-mouthed and yellow-toothed. Horses – golden brown, chestnut, grey, black and swishy-tailed piebalds, all brown and white and beautiful. A barrow, full of glistening red ripe tomatoes, stands alongside a twin piled high with yellow lemons, ripe red apples, long green cucumber and bunches of lovely bananas.

"Now there's a colourful sight," say I. I follow a gorgeous gleaming soldier, his buttons golden, tunic scarlet, snow-white gloves upon his hands, bright blue trousers striped with red, a gleaming helmet on his handsome head. What a fine figure he cuts! I stretch my legs and strive to match his pace. "Join the army and see the world!"

"I'll do just that!"

The gallant soldier steps into the recruiting office, and my immature poetic train of thought stops dead. "Fuck shitty old Liverpool! I'll see the great big world. I know it's there – I've seen it on the movies."

A weary-looking corporal, head uncapped, pencil behind his ear, deep red ring upon his forehead, raises up his close-cropped head. "What do you want, kid?"

"I want to join the army and see the world!"

"How old are you?"

"Fourteen and two days."

"Go in there!" he points.

What luck! The gleaming handsome soldier sits at an empty, blanket-covered desk. He smiles. His handsome looks send shivers down my spine. He will seduce me! I know it!

"Name?"

"Jackie, Jack Robinson, sir."

"School?"

"St Jude's."

"Parents' consent?"

"I can get that, sir."

A smell of Brasso hits my nostrils. The smell of pencil – black graphite, just like school. Musty papers on the shelves. Maps pinned on the walls. A spirit of adventure stirs the blood in my veins. I smile.

"Go behind the screen and take your clothes off."

"All of them?"

"Yes. I need to weigh you. You'll find a robe in one of the cubicles. Slip it on if you feel cold."

There is a row of small cubicles behind the screen door, a brightly-polished brass clothes-hook on each door, a hanging woollen robe on every hook and a smell of Johnson's floor wax everywhere.

A huge platform scale stands silent on the floor, its long brass needle pointing to zero. A tall wooden stand, complete with sliding oak-stained deal, rests firm against the wall. Markings painted on the stand tell me that this is used for measuring one's height. I smile and take my clothes off.

It was almost like being in the swimming bath locker-room.

"Come along, young man. Don't be shy. Slip the robe off and step on the scale." He gives my bottom a friendly little smack. My dickie rises. I cover it with my hand and step up on the platform.

"Face this way!"

I turn and face the handsome man, my boyish palm for a fig leaf.

"You seem sound enough." He squiggles on a clipboard in his hand. "Step beneath the sliding scale. Hands to your side. Feet flat on the floor – don't play tippy toes with me. I must have it right." The warm trouser-leg touches my young and very firm erection as he slides the measure to my head.

"Good lad!" he says. He makes another squiggle with his pen. "Raise your arms above your head."

I obey. He looks into my armpits. "No hair?" he says aloud. "Don't get dressed. I'm sending you into the M.O."

"The M.O.?" I ask, puzzled.

"The doctor, sonny. Put the robe over your shoulders and sit in a cubicle." I place the robe over my shoulders, empty sleeves dangling at my side.

He rumples my curls. "You'll have no trouble. You're a fine young healthy boy." The friendly hand in my hair makes me tremble, and the wicked sexual thoughts get worse.

A door of gleaming polished oak, brass knobbed and sturdy in its painted frame, swings open and the smell of hospital invades my nose. The erection dies at once and a voice calls out, "Send him in!"

The M.O. looks me up and down. "Open your mouth!" he says. "Good! Can you read the card on the wall?"

"Yes sir!" I read aloud and very fast.

He leans a card against my eye. "Read once more," he says. "Now the other eye."

I read. I name some colours on a plaque.

"Good! Very good!" A cold stethoscope touches my bare breast. "A fine young boy," he says. "Bend over and touch your toes."

I bend.

He looks up my bottom. "Stand up. Look me in the eye," he says and squeezes my testicles in a cold medical hand.

"Cough!"

I cough.

"Fine! Any insanity in the family?"

"No." I laugh at such an unexpected question, think about my crazy old man and say again, "No sir!"

"Tuberculosis?"

"Who, me?"

"In the family?"

"No sir!"

"Have you ever been sick?"

"No sir! Never in my life!"

He looks at the vaccination scars upon my upper arm, peers down my ears with an instrument, pulls at the hair on my head, looks closely at my feet. "Stand upon your tip-toes." He seems satisfied at last, smiles at me and says, "Do you know about girls?"

"Not much, sir."

"Keep away from them. Wait until you are older!"

"Yes sir!"

"You can go now. The sergeant will look after you."

"The sergeant," I think to myself. "Which one is he?" The answer comes to me the moment I slip the robe from my shoulders.

"Don't get dressed," he says. "Put the robe on and sit in my office. I want a few words with you." It's the handsome recruiting officer, all scarlet and blue and gorgeous glitter. I thought he looked so splendid that he must have been at least a general or a major.

"Now listen carefully. . . . Jackie, isn't it?"

"Yes sir."

"Once you have taken the oath, been sworn in, got your parents' consent and taken the shilling, there is no turning back! You are in for sixteen long years! Do you understand?"

"Yes."

"Think about it. You sign on for twelve years, but the first four do not count because it is boy service. Understand?"

"Yes."

"You have passed the medical test. You bring the blue paper back tomorrow with a signature on it. I swear you in and that is you finished! You are a soldier from that moment on! A real soldier!"

"I want to be a soldier," I say. "I'll be here on the doorstep in the morning, paper signed and ready to go."

"Were you any good in school, sonny?"

"Not bad. I'm a good swimmer. I box and play football for the school team."

"How would you like to go to a wonderful place where they teach you riding, swimming, fencing, gymnastics and music?"

"Sounds like paradise."

"It's the Boys' Battery at Woolwich. But it's going to be tough with your educational background. St Jude's is not quite the standard we require. I'll have to give you some exam papers. Do your best, lad. Otherwise you will be just an ordinary band boy in an infantry regiment full of soldiers. "What do you say?"

"Give me the exam papers. I'll take them home and complete them tonight," I say, bursting with enthusiasm.

"Ah! Lad!!!" he stroked my hair. "Get dressed. If you fail the exams, I'll take you home and polish your weak points myself. I'll make sure you pass. Do you understand?"

"Yes. It's very clear."

He leans back in his chair. "It's a wonderful opportunity for a lad like you. Run along and get dressed," he says, as if he was really going to do me a favour.

I fly, scramble into my clothes, lace my good brown sturdy shoes, run to his polished office door and knock.

"Enter!" I poke my head in and smile at him. "What time do you close?" I shout.

"Six o'clock tonight," replies the handsome soldier man.

"I'll be back by then with my parents' consent." I take the bright blue paper from his desk, scoop up the exam papers and scoot away.

A rattling old tramcar, all cream and rusty chocolate brown, takes me swiftly from the grey old town and drops me near my mother's home.

"Ma!" I look her in the eye. "I've joined the army. You have to sign this form." She scribbles "Lizzie Robinson" on the bright blue paper and throws it on the dirty kitchen table. I grab the flimsy passport to the whole wide world and run.

Lord Nelson Street: the sign above the door – will he still be there? It's getting late. . . almost six o'clock. The handsome man is all alone. Everyone else has gone. "Hello young man," he says. "I've been expecting you."

"My papers." I thrust the forms upon his desk.

"I only need this one, Jackie."

"Just the exam papers to worry about? I can get through that lot easily. I looked through them on the tram."

"I'll help you with some of the tricky ones if you like."

"Now?" I ask hopefully.

"Unless you want to go!" he says, winking his bright blue eye.

"No. If you think you can help me. . ."

"When the Education Officer looks at your papers, he can tell how suitable you are. But there are some things that may knock you out before the bell goes. Make yourself comfortable at my desk and I'll point them out." He leaves the room and locks the outer door. I know he's going to seduce me – I just knew it all the time! Shall I act coy? Play the innocent virgin? Struggle just a tiny bit? Wiggle with delight? We sit together, shoulders touching. . .

"Take this simple question – 'What are your hobbies?' What would you put in that column, Jackie?"

"Swimming, football, boxing."

"Next question – 'What are your sports?' Any special preference?"

"I would have to write the same things again," say I.

"Let's go back to hobbies, Jackie – you with me?"

"Yep. Going to the pictures." My mind, my wicked mind says, 'No – I musn't think of Eggy'. "Chess!" I say aloud and clear.

"Good! That's the sort of thing. Forget about the pictures. Do you read?"

"Everything I can lay my hands on."

"Like what?"

"Comics, books from the library, the morning paper, film star magazines. . ."

"Have you read any of Robert Louis Stevenson?"

"Yes, and seen the picture. He wrote 'Treasure Island'."

"Well, put down literature. Good books! Don't mention comics. Do you like poetry?"

"I love poetry."

"How about music?"

"I love it!"

"Gilbert and Sullivan?"

"Yes, we sang all that stuff in school."

"Right! That's enough. You know how to fill it in now but I'll pencil the columns in for you, and you go over it later. You got it all in that handsome little head of yours?"

"Yes. I'll make a good job of it. I'll stay up all night if neccessary."

"Would you like to jump on the scales again? I think I made a mistake when I weighed you. Can't be too careful can we?" he winks.

My dickie just stood up in my knickers!

"With my clothes off?" I say hopefully.

"Yes. I'll help you if you wish. Are you in a hurry?"

"No." Such a simple word.

"Slip your shoes off. Come along."

The platform scale looks cold and bare. His gentle hand moves in my hair. "Let me have the shirt off, son. Lift up your arms."

"My shorts?" I say, fingers ready at the waistband.

"What do you think, Jackie?"

I have them halfway down my legs. "I suppose it will be better if I take them off. Are you going to measure me again?" I slip out of my grey school shorts and stand before the handsome soldier, stiff dickie straining at my knickers. I smile at him and blush.

He reaches out and pulls my flimsy garment from me. "You don't have to hide it this time," he says.

"I was shy this morning."

"You are not shy now. Why?"

"Because I like you. I know you want to look at me. Do you like me?"

He strokes my cheek, tousles my hair and opens his trouser front. He knows exactly what I am: a sexy boy who likes men. The sergeant seems to like kissing. Friendly kisses mean a lot to me. He kisses my forehead, throws a dressing-gown over my shoulders and leads me by the hand into another room.

I want him to make love to me. He has a wonderful penis – thick, long and exciting. I take it in my hand and play with it.

"No," he says pushing my hand away. "Lie down on the couch."

It's more like a doctor's examination bench – all shiny leather, a hinged pillow and a cold, white linen covering.

He slips the gown from my shoulders, places it on the bench and watches me settle down. I lie on my belly. He removes his shoes and trousers. It looks strange: I'm not used to half-dressed lovers, but I soon relax when his firm hands begin to massage my shoulders.

"You're a sexy young devil," he whispers, rubbing some kind of oil into my shoulder-blades – massage, rub, knead and stroke. The slippy fluid runs into the hollow of my firm young spine and trickles into the lower parts. Pleasure, sensation, luxury: I just lie beneath his searching fingers and wallow in it. He pushes my legs apart, places his little finger in the most intimate spot and tickles me.

My bottom rises invitingly. He slaps it down, turns me on my back and rubs the oil into my chest. It's out of this world! He kisses the boyish nipples on my breasts and tweaks my stiffened pigeon.

"Kiss me."

He kisses me. I sit up and see the great erection in his hand. The sergeant certainly knows how to make love to boys like me. Slippy with rubbing oils, mucus escaping from the tip of his sexual organ, he penetrates and pushes it home, smiling into my bright blue eyes like a man loves a girl.

Perhaps a fine young soldier boy shouldn't ask for kisses, but I have to; I just have to be kissed and loved. He's gentle, smothers me with friendly kisses, helps me to dress and kisses me goodbye in his little office.

A great feeling of pleasure and security washes over me. I'm so happy and excited that I run all the way to the Pier Head, buy a penny ticket and take the ferry across the

Mersey.

Seated in the warmth of the ferry-boat saloon, I start work on the exam papers. They look simple enough, so I take Eggy's Woolworth fountain pen from my pocket and go over the pencilled entries. Foreign languages? Some French. Hobbies? Chess, literature, music, cycling. Sports and pastimes? Boxing and all physical sports. "How about kissing Eggy's bum?" I think. "That would be a nice pastime. Jesus, I'm going to miss him! I'd better call on him and tell him I've joined the army. God knows how I'm going to break the news to Eddie. . ."

What can I do about it? I just have to get away! I must! The sums are easy. I finish them as we hit the pier.

"Rock Ferry! All ashore for Rock Ferry! The gnarled old mariners coil the giant ropes, as thick as a man's leg, drop the great wide wooden gangways and watch the passengers step ashore. "What are you doing, boy? You should be ashore."

"I'm doing my entrance exam for the army, sir. May I stay on the boat?"

"All right, lad," says the gruff old skipper. He rolls across the heaving deck and leaves me at my work. On and on I go – history, geography – all about France and Belgium. . . The Great War. . . that's easy.

"All ashore for the Pier Head! Liverpool and the Pier Head!" A voice in my ear: "Still at it, lad?" asks the old salt.

"Yes sir!" I reply and smile.

"Here's a bar of chocolate for you!"

"Thank you, sir," I say and wolf the penny Cadbury.

The old skipper is interested. "How are you doing, lad?"

"I'm stumped! I'll have to go to the library tomorrow," I say.

"What's the problem?" asks the friendly old guy.

"Nelson! Lord Nelson – where did Horatio Nelson lose his right arm? What a daft question!"

"A lad like you should join the navy!" He shows his tattooed muscular arm. "I sailed before the mast," he says. "I went to sea as a boy of ten. Square-riggers, schooners, everything! I was a real sailor, not a bloody ferry-boat skipper! You'll find out everything you need to know about Nelson at the Maritime Museum."

Four times across the Mersey for one penny! I was all through! Nelson could wait until tomorrow. He could wait until he got his eye back for all I cared.

Up through Ikey Moses' coalyard, past the ragged, black-faced coal boys, white-eyed and grimy, jackets slit from carrying sacks on their muscular young backs. They scared me, these pitch black lines of heaving boys.

Margaret Street. . . the swimming baths. . . Eggy's momma just around the corner. At last! I knocked at the door.

"Hello, Jackie! Come in dear," said his charming mother.

Eggy rushed down the stairs. "There you are! Where have you been all day? I've been looking for you."

"On the ferry boat for a couple of hours. I'm joining the army!"

"Don't talk daft! Mam's getting me a job in town. She said I can stay with Uncle Paul all week. Do you like my longees?" he asked proudly.

I'd forgotten all about long trousers. "Yes. You look all grown-up. Very smart indeed."

His momma put her arm about him and gave him a little hug. "He does look nice in long trousers. When are you getting some?"

"At the weekend if I'm lucky. Army trousers! I've joined the army! I really have," I said determinedly.

"You must be potty!" shouted my young friend.

"What's wrong with being a soldier? They get holidays you know. I can come and visit you."

His momma stroked his nice pink cheek. "Come and stay wih us, Jackie. You stay with us when you get away on leave. Timmy's going to miss you."

"Don't worry about me. I'm looking forward to it! I think I'm going to like it. The school bit bothers me though."

"What kind of school?" asked Eggy.

"Army school! I have to attend school until I'm eighteen."

They knew I meant it then. Eggy read the forms I'd worked on and saw the copy of the attestation form. "Twelve years! That's a lifetime!"

I offered him the borrowed pen.

"Keep it, Jackie. You can have my leather satchel too. I won't need it any more. Do you want to stay with me tonight?" A thought flashed through my mind – how could I

face Eddie? Christ! He'd be upset. I shouldn't have done it. . .
I haven't been sworn in yet. . . Balls!

"I'd love to stay, Eggy. Can we call on Eddie together?" I
asked.

"I don't know how to break the news. I'll have to stay with
you tonight, Eggy. Jesus! Eddie will be very upset. Tell your
mam we might be late home."

My curly-headed schoolfriend kissed his mam. We ran
down the street laughing.

"You should have seen my old lady's bleedin' face," I
shouted as we flew through the jigger.

"What did she say?"

"Fuck all! She signed the paper! I'm a fuckin' soldier!"

"You could get a job with me. It's not too late, Jack."

"I've got to go, Eggy. I've just got to. I'm so thrilled about
it!"

We skipped aboard a passing tram and skipped off the
speeding monster as it rattled down near Eddie's home.

"Tell him I'm staying with you tonight. I can't face him."

"He won't mind, will he?"

"No. He thinks you're nice!"

"He's never spoken to me in his life!"

"He sees you with me on the way to school. He knows all
about us!"

"Everything?"

"Of course! Me, you, Paul! Everything! I tell him everything."

"Not about Paul screwing you, surely?"

"No, no, no. . . that's private. He knows you and I have
been poking each other and he knows you sleep with Paul."

I open the front door. Better make a pot of tea. He'll be
home any minute.

The silver tea tray, three cups and saucers, lumps of sugar
in the bowl, three gleaming silver spoons and Eddie smiling
at my guest. "You brought your friend at last! Hello young
man. Timmy, isn't it?"

I missed my hug. "It's okay, Eddie. You can give me a hug
in front of Tim. He understands. He wants me to stay with
him tonight. We've got some things to take care of in town
and need to make an early start."

Eddie hugged me to his lumpy buttons and kissed the tip

of my nose.

"Give Timmy a hug," I said. "We'll all be more comfortable then."

Eggy got a kiss on the cheek. It looked lovely. I was glad in a way.

"You're a very quiet boy, Timmy."

Eggy smiled and poured the tea. "I just feel strange in long trousers. I'm not really quiet or anything like that."

"He's just lovely," I said, putting my arm around him. "You don't mind, do you Eddie?"

"Don't be silly. Why should I mind? You've been kissing and loving all your lives. I'm going to get changed. You are staying for a bit, I hope."

"We can stay till midnight if you like," I said, trying to be nice.

"Not if you don't want to. Enjoy your freedom, son. I bet you're glad you left school. What did you do with yourself today?"

I didn't like telling him lies. "Nothing much. I went through Ikey Moses' old coal yard. I was taking a short cut to Eggy's."

"Keep away from those lads," he said and went upstairs.

"Jesus! I almost told him. . ."

"Why didn't you?"

"I don't know. Put the bleedin' wireless on. . ."

Eddie gave us a cuddle before we left. It was eleven thirty and the kids were still on the streets, swinging punctured corn-beef cans filled with flaming coals around their heads. Wire-handled milk cans, bean cans. . . Kneeling, bare-legged on the freezing streets, warming their hands at the red hot coals. . .

Eggy linked my arm as we hurried home. "Fuckin' winter warmers! I'll be your winter warmer tonight, Jackie boy! Your friend Eddie made me horny for you," he whispered.

"Mmmm! There's one thing we haven't done together, Eggy. Should we go all the way tonight? Do everything!"

"Do you want it in your mouth?"

"Do you?"

"Let's run – we'll miss the friggin' tramcar."

"Eggy?"

"Yeah?"

"What do you know about Nelson?"

"Fuck all! He had one eye, one arm and one arsehole! That's all I know!"

We get up early and eat a healthy breakfast of fried black pudding, crispy bacon and spicy tomato sausage. The smell of the bakehouse greets our nostrils as the early morning shoppers pick up their oven-bottomed loaves and we stroll into the city arm in arm.

I ask him to come into the recruiting office with me but he won't. "I'll wait outside," he says sensibly.

"The recruiting officer has got a dick like a donkey."

"Well, you can have it," says my friend.

"You sure I can't tempt you?" I reply, as if I didn't know.

"Balls! I'll wait outside," says Eggy, not knowing what he was missing.

"My entrance exam," I say to the smiling seducer. "There's one question unanswered, but I can get that one for you after the public library opens."

"What's the question?"

"Nelson's arm."

"Everyone knows that."

"I bet you don't, sir."

"Horatio Nelson: born 1758, died 1805. Lost his right arm at Santa Cruz, 1798."

"I'd better write that down then."

"You've done well, sonny. Are you ready to take the plunge?"

"Yes sir!"

"Read this card."

"I swear. . ."

"Take this shilling. Keep it. It's yours."

"Thank you." I put the silver shilling in my trouser pocket.

"You're in the army now," says the horny handsome sergeant. "You leave for Woolwich Arsenal at the weekend. You are in Borgard section, Boys' Battery, Royal Regiment of Artillery. Consider yourself lucky! You might have finished up in the King's Liverpool Regiment. Call in at the weekend and I'll give you a railway warrant. Unless you wish to call in just for a visit. . ."

"Thank you, sir. See you later," I say, winking slyly.

Eggy smiles at me. "All over?"

"Yep. I've got a shilling. Wanna come to the pictures with me?"

"No. I want you to get some long trousers. The London boys might laugh at you in shorts."

"I've never worn longees in my life!"

"You'll have to, Jackie. The people in the south are different than us. I know. Uncle Paul has been there lots of times. Everything is modern and clean. Big lads like us wear trousers, not shorts. Paul's taking me to London. . . I hope."

"If Paul takes you to London, Eggy, it won't be to put trousers on you!"

Paddy's Market seems the best place to strike a bargain, so we hit the dirty streets, sneak along the infamous Scotland Road and walk into the market-place. My own little world! Coolies, dishpan hats, straw boaters, button boots and big fat women's stinking stays.

"'Ow much for the trousers, wack?" I shout across the stall.

"I'll take a bob!" says the man.

"Piss off! They're not worth last year's fuckin' *Echo*!"

"Give us a tanner!" says the man.

"Make it three pence, wack! I'm skint!" I say, turning out my pockets.

"Show us the three pence. . . Right! Take the kecks! Fly bastard!"

"Where did you learn all that lot?" asks Eggy.

"I work here!"

"Threepence for a pair of trousers!"

"I only need them for one day."

"They're quite good. I hope they're clean!"

"So do I. They're going in your satchel when we get home."

"I'll get me mam to wash them for you."

"Thanks, Eggy. You're a pal."

Eddie couldn't take it. I kissed him and came right out with it.

"I've joined the army!"

"Don't be silly. You only left school two days ago."

"I don't tell lies, Eddie. Not to you. . ."

"You're only a child!" he stormed.

"I'm in the army! I'm sworn in and leave for Woolwich Arsenal at the weekend," I said, feeling mean.

"But you're only a boy!"

"I'm a soldier boy! I've taken the King's shilling."

"Holy Jesus!"

"Don't be sad, Eddie – please don't cry. . ." I wiped away his tears, made him a pot of tea, and sat with him, arm around his shoulder.

"What's going to become of you? It's all so stupid! A homosexual boy of fourteen in the army! There'll be all kinds of men after you!"

"I'm not a homosexual! I'm a boy! Your boy! I love you."

"Jackie, Jackie! What the hell have you done?"

"I'll get a good education, Eddie. I want to go out into the world! I'll always love you. . . always."

"Why? Why?"

"I don't know. . . Take me to bed. . . It's not the end of the world!" I still felt mean, sorry.

Eddie held my hand in the comfort of our bed. He stroked my damp hair. "Do you feel miserable?" he asked.

"Yes."

"You mustn't feel bad about it. If you really were my son, I would still have to let you go. You have a life of your own to live. Go out and enjoy it, lad. . ."

CHAPTER TEN

Drummer Boy

"Goodbye Eggy!"

"We've got a few more minutes yet." He gripped my hand. It was very early in the morning at Lime Street railway station, full of grime and sooty steam. "I won't be seeing you for a long time, Jackie. Let's say goodbye in the lavatory. The guard will blow his whistle before the train pulls out."

"Hurry then. I'm going to miss that warm old bed of yours." A little cuddle behind the narrow toilet door, a kiss on the lips, Eggy's old school satchel clutched in my hand, and a last embrace.

"We've had some great times together, kid. I'll write to you every week. One last favour before you go. . . please?"

"Anything! Whatever you want, Jack."

"Eddie is going to be sad. Take this key – see he don't get lonely. . ." The gush of steam and a shrill piping noise made me jump. "He's a lonely man, Eggy. He'll miss me. Will you call and see him? Make friends with him?"

Eggy hugged me very close. "Let's get out of here," he said. "I'll make friends with him. I know he likes me."

"He likes boys. . . needs a boy about the place. I hope you understand. Don't spoil your friendship with Paul. Eddie thinks you're lovely. Would you sleep with him and keep him company once or twice a week?"

"I'll love him for you, Jackie. Don't worry about it."

"Call around tomorrow night and tell him I forgot to leave the key. Don't give it back to him. I know you'll cheer him up. Tell him I love him, won't you?"

The sound of the whistle. . .

"Gotta go, Jackie."

"So long, kid!"

Life was calling! Eggy, just a tiny figure on the platform. . .

out of sight now.

"I'm on my way, on an express train. . . lucky old me," I thought. "I'm not scared – well, just a bit. . . not really *scared*. I wonder what it's going to be like?"

Rich green fields fly past the grimy windows. Quiet little villages seem to vanish in a flash and thousands of dirty old telegraph poles blur past my eyes. My first long journey on a train: Eggy's momma has packed some home-made cake and sandwiches for me. What a lovely woman! What a handsome, gorgeous son. I'm going to miss them.

I find a copy of this week's *Hotspur* and a couple of copies of the *Rover* in the satchel. No one will mind if I read them. I like the *Hotspur*. I wonder if the boys in the army read comics?

I hope they don't all talk posh. The fencing lessons sound interesting. Maybe it will be fun! I could be a second Douglas Fairbanks! Some hope! My mind is full of crazy thoughts. The last time I had seen Douglas Fairbanks in the movies was in a silent film at "The Penny Lytton" – the only picture house I had not bothered to sneak into. It only cost one penny and they still showed silent movies. Would I ever get into the "Lousy Lytton" again?

A stroll along the corridor to stretch my legs, poke my nose into the first-class compartments and have a pee in the posh first-class toilet. It smelled of tart's perfume and powder. A town named Rugby flashed by and it made me wonder if the army kids played rugby. I hoped not because I would never understand the silly game as long as I had a tongue in my head. My head! The army would cut my nice curls off!

Journey's end at last! A very handsome soldier man, all blue and gold and glittering chain, rich red stripes and clanking, burnished silver spurs, met me at Woolwich station, beckoning me with his white-gloved forefinger.

"What's your name, boy?"

"Jackie. . . Jack Robinson, sir!"

"You're the one. This way! We haven't got all day! You're in the army now!"

"Yes sir!" I said, trying to keep up with this dazzling, awe-inspiring figure – stretching my legs, stepping out and clutching Eggy's school bag to my chest.

"I like your uniform, sir. Will I get one like that?"

"You need a haircut! Do you know the name of your regiment?"

"Yes sir!"

"It's the pride of the British Army! This is a dress uniform. You can have one exactly like this when you have the money to pay for it. Understand?"

"No sir." Unfriendly devil!

"Step out! We're almost there. . ."

I could hear them. . . It sounded like the charge of the light brigade! Horses thundering, thundering. . . Thundering horse and light gun carriage! Wow! There they were! Bright-faced boys in chin-strapped army caps, thundering across the hardened winter ground, booted and spur-clad, sparkling eyed!

"Fucking hell!" I thought. "I wish Eggy could see this lot. . . what a fucking sight!" I must start speaking nicely – change my ways and be a good lad.

We reached the barrack square. A section of pink-cheeked marching boys, arms swinging, heads on high, proud lads with puffed-out chests marched on. I liked the look of their uniforms: riding britches and spurs, military whip in hand, swinging like a swagger cane.

Music surged from a line of handsome boys about two years older than me – big boys, some of them about seventeen, long silver trumpets at the lip. A music teacher was obviously in charge. Just like the horny recruiting sergeant had said: "Music. . . they'll teach you about music, riding and sports. . ." The rattle of drumsticks reminds me of the boy scouts. A rat-a-tat-tat a rat-a-tat-tat! You're in the army now!

There was so much activity going on that I could not quite absorb it all at once. However, they looked carefree and happy. A strange piping voice called out and suddenly the parade ground was one great mass of scrambling boys.

They passed me by without a glance; no doubt it was supper time and they were hungry. I know I was.

A friendly sergeant fed me, piled me up with army gear and showed me to a bed. It had been very exciting but apart from the instructions given, no one else had spoken to me in the noisy barrack room. I was glad to get to bed; after all, it had been a long weary day. A sweet trumpet filled the air with music and all the lights went out.

It was very lonely in my little cot, but my sweet friend Eggy came to me, slipped his gentle hand around my waist and whispered, "I love you, Jackie boy." It was all so real! I felt his gentle fingers, smelt the fragrance of his momma's shampoo in his curly hair, dickie stiff on my belly. I awoke and shouted out. . .

"What's wrong, kid?" asked a friendly voice at my side. "Are you homesick?"

"No. I'm okay. I must have been dreaming."

The boy sat on the edge of my cot. "Don't be afraid to cry," he said. "Nobody will laugh at you. Everyone feels like that on the first night."

"I ain't crying. I was dreaming."

"How old are you?" asked the friendly voice.

"Fourteen," I replied, still troubled by the realistic dream.

"I'm sixteen. I've been here two years. What's your name?"

"Jackie," I said in the darkness of the barrack room.

"I'm Chesty," said the friendly voice. "My friends call me Chesty."

"Do you like it here?" I asked him.

"Yes. It's great! You'll like it. All the kids are smashing in this section. Goodnight, kid. You'll be alright tomorrow." Chesty jumped into his bed, and I fell asleep playing with my dickie and thinking about Eggy.

The simple noisy routine of barrack-room life pleased me, and I soon got the hang of things. Nobody wore pyjamas – most of the kids slept in army shirts. The kids were boisterous and funny, and shirt tails, bare bottoms and little fat pigeons flashed around the barrack room at night. Big boys wrestled half-naked on the younger ones' beds and there were pillow fights, bums and big swinging dickies all over the place. I had been sleeping in my undershorts but once I got used to the free and easy ways, I jumped into bed in the nude, my usual sleeping habit.

Chesty smiled at me from the next cot. "You're settling down then?" he said.

"Yes," I replied. "I'm settling in just swell."

"'Night, kid."

The trumpet sounded lights out; I played with my dickie, thought of sweet Eggy and splashed all over my belly. Boys walked barefoot and shirt-tailed to the beds of others.

The comic books I had been reading all my life were full of stories about boys who lived, ate, slept and spent their lives in posh public schools. They filled my heart with joy, but they did not cater for the likes of me. They were not part of the real world: theirs was a world of make believe, a world of dormitories, high jinks, house-masters, prep schools, cads, bounders, heroes and happy days on the cricket pitches and rugger fields of Merrie England! Where the hell was that? Did they only think of kids from wealthy families? Why did they not produce real stories? How about the kids who got a pair of roller skates for Christmas, but couldn't use them because they had no shoes and stockings?

Weary Willie and Tired Tim: they were real and they appeared on the front page of *Funny Wonder*, a penny comic. However, they were shown as ridiculous figures of fun, always searching for a plate of sausage and mash, begging outside the gleaming doorway of the Ritz hotel and picking half-smoked cigar-ends from the gutters. No doubt the rich lads from the public schools of Merrie England thought of these two characters in much the same way I thought of them. But the two comic figures existed in real life; Liverpool was full of Weary Willies and all kinds of unfortunate bastards.

Suddenly, a mighty hand had sucked me from the stench of Liverpool and all its poverty and set me down in a brand new world. It was wonderful! All my boyhood dreams had come true. I was in a posh public school right out of the pages of my comic books. But the lessons were much more exciting: fencing with real swords, padded protective clothing, a wonderful fencing master. Salute, kiss the hilt of your weapon, on guard! Thrust and parry. . . Music lessons in the music room. Trumpet lessons in an enormous shed. Horse riding on the plains and in the "rodeo". Bright modern classrooms and excellent teachers from the Army Education Corps. Art, history and geography and every possible advantage at my fingertips.

I was Kim, the boy from the pages of Rudyard Kipling. Sure, I was from a different background than most of the boys but, like Kim, I could make a living while they starved to death if it came to the push. Fortunately, there was no class distinction. Everybody dressed the same, looked the same and acted like the fine young men they were.

God knows how many boys there were in the battery. Men did not exist. It was a boys' battery. True, we had teachers, instructors, bombardiers and sergeants, but they simply trained us by day, frightened the life out of us and sent spittle flying into our rosy cheeks.

Our day ended at four o'clock and the men simply vanished. Some went to their homes in married quarters and others went about their daily lives, but we did not see them. Men were not allowed to mix with boys.

Some dormitories had a little room near the door entrance and in this room there lived a man, a bombardier, housemaster, mother, father, nurse and anything you wished him to be according to your specific problem. Other dormitories were supervised by a senior boy soldier. Naturally enough, he was one of us, a boy who had assumed the *toga virilis*, mature, manly and in full bloom: almost a man. The lads worshipped such boys.

Out of bed at six a.m., towel around your naked waist, toothbrush in hand; wash your body, scrub your teeth, take a piss; comb your hair, drag your knickers on, climb into a dreadful suit of canvas and fly to the parade ground for inspection.

Breakfast! My first breakfast was fried fish and chips. Fish and chips for breakfast! I couldn't believe it. Lovely crusty bread, fresh butter, mugs of milk and scalding tea, plenty of everything. If you wanted a second helping, you stood to attention in front of your empty plate. A dining-room orderly took the plate and filled it up. That was it: big eats!

I loved every second and could hardly believe my ears when a bombardier taught me how to salute for my pay packet.

"Pay! We get paid?"

"Seven shillings and sixpence a week, lad. Three bob in your hand and the rest in your bank account, or credits. You'll need it when you go on leave for a holiday."

Who wanted to leave such a wonderland? Not I. Clean beds, no fleas, fresh laundry and warm blankets: neither school nor army, but a combination of all things that were important to my new life. Playing fields, gymnasiums, football, boxing, hockey and every sport in the world. Ping-pong in the recreation room. What the hell was ping-pong? Darts: I had never seen a game of darts. People in my part of the country did not play darts. Darts were not introduced into Liverpool until long after the Second World War.

We were real soldiers and subject to King's Rules and Regulations. Cowardice in the face of the enemy – death by firing squad. Stealing from a comrade, stealing rations, water, ammunition in time of war – death by firing squad. These were out-dated regulations. Nevertheless, they existed and could be put to use.

The boys did not steal. It was unheard of.

The punishment for smoking was ten strokes of the cane on your bare bottom. It took place in the gym and in full view of your comrades. Naturally enough, none of the kids used cigarettes.

The youngest among us were not allowed out of barracks, for it was a real barracks and probably the only boys' battery in the greedy British Empire that stretched its grasping fingers across the world, plundering, exploiting and dealing out death and destruction. When the instructors were satisfied with a lad's progress, and providing the boy was well trained and disciplined, he could go into town, but not alone. Twos and threes were the standing orders.

Early to bed and early to rise. Half-day Wednesday, half-day on Saturday and complete freedom on Sunday. . . after church parade. That's when it hit you! Sunday church parade. Fantastic! The whole population of Woolwich turned out to watch us. The majestic figure of the tall drum-major. Glittering officers on gorgeous steeds, gleaming swords and belts. The band and drums in all its glory, music pounding in your ear. Eyes front! Throw your skinny chest out and smile. The whole world is looking at you, boy! You're the mighty British Empire!

Boys came from all over the world; lads from military families. They sat around in little groups and talked of their homes in faraway places: India, Africa, Malta, Gibraltar, Palestine and the British West Indies.

It is possible that they talked about girls, but I was not interested in the opposite sex. I loved to watch a senior boy with an arm around his young friend's shoulder, soft music in the room, a mouth organ, a muted trumpet-piece and gentle voices singing. Welsh boys could sing like angels and often led a sad, sad song before lights out. It was beautiful! Close your eyes my little drummer boy. Lights out was sounded long ago. . . Go to sleep my little drummer boy and dream of all your friends and foe. . .

Dear Eggy,
    Always thinking about you. Give my love to your mam and our friends. Next time we meet I shall be in my uniform and steel spurs. There are shiny buses on the streets of London. I like it here. We ride real hunters and war-horses. There are ferry boats, but not like those on the Mersey. Please send me a photograph of yourself. I will do the same.
  So long!
  Jack.

Of course I thought about Eddie and was going to write him a nice long letter. However, I had many things to learn, to adjust to my new environment and fit in with lads from a "better" station in life who spoke strange tongues and had different habits. Some of the kids from military backgrounds could speak four or five languages. It came naturally to them, because they'd spent their childhood in different countries. These youngsters were on the way to Sandhurst and other military academies. But they weren't all from army homes. Some of the lads were from families who wished to give their son a good education but could not afford the expense of an English public school.

I met only one boy from Liverpool, a kid named Quigley, a sixteen year old who could handle the most impossible horses. He was a sarcastic big-head, but one had to admire him for his ability.

Another boy wore silk pyjamas and dressing-gown, and spoke like the Prince of Wales. Everyone made fun of him, but he didn't care a damn. He simply played his classical music on an old wind-up gramophone and minded his own business. He was a real gentleman. However, a few weeks in such lovely surroundings would not turn me into a young gentleman. It would take a thousand years!

Different lads had different titles: Drummer, Trumpeter, Boy. Boy was the lowest form of animal life in the British Army.

"Boy Robinson!" a voice called out.

"That's me."

"Bombardier!"

"That's me, Bombardier."

He tossed me a letter and it landed on my bed. Toby, the boy in the opposite bunk from me, got two letters every day. However, this was the first letter I had ever received in my life. I opened it and the tears began to flow. Kick me, beat me, punch my silly head and I would not shed a tear, but this was a new experience for me. I couldn't see the words on the stupid pages; only the photograph of Eggy and Eddie side by side. They looked so wonderful together!

Toby threw me a towel and called me to his bunk. "Dry your tears and sit with me," he said quietly. Chesty joined us.

"Everyone cries when they get their first letter from home," he said soothingly. "It's alright. Nobody will laugh at you."

The comradeship made up for almost anything. Chesty looked at the photograph. "Is that your dad?" he asked.

"Yes," I lied.

"And your brother? He looks like you."

"My friend. . . that's my friend," I said, still snivelling.

The next day we played football and I really had a work-out, scored two goals and got covered in mud. It was just like being in paradise. Chesty grabbed me in the shower, put his big golden-skinned body right close up to me and kissed the tip of my nose.

"You are a real beauty!" he said. "Do you like me?"

"Do you want to make friends with me, Chesty?"

"I kissed you, didn't I? You horny bugger!"

"I let you, didn't I? Horny bugger yourself! I've never seen such a big one in my life," I said, feeling very happy.

"Let's go in a tub room and lock the door." He gripped my stiffened dickie, kissed my nose again and tried to force me from the shower.

"No," I whispered, taking his great erection in my hands.

"We'll get into trouble."

"We will if we stay here. Any cunt might walk in," said the boy.

"Piss off, Chesty. I like you, but I'm not going to ruin my army life. I like being a soldier."

"Come with me – I'm dying for a wank off. . . please!"

"Are you sure it's safe?"

"Yes! All the kids have a bit of fun in the tub rooms. It's easy with the door locked."

Chesty closed the bathroom door, turned on the taps and stood up in the tub. "Come on, Jackie. I'm horny for you."

"I'm horny for you," I replied, taking his lovely big dick.

"You've got lovely long eyelashes, Jackie. Pull me off!"

"You pull mine then," I whispered, pulling his great pointed dick.

"Is that all you want? You did let me kiss you. . ." We clung together rubbing brown wet bellies and looking into each other's eyes. "Let me bum you?" he said, pleading in his voice.

"No," I said. "I'm a fuckin' soldier boy, not a bum boy!"

"Christ! You let me kiss you!"

"Just a kiss, Chesty. A couple of little kisses. Tell anyone about this and I'll kick you in the balls next time we play football."

Chesty put his strong brown arms round me, and it finished. "Jesus, I've spunked all over you. . ."

"Let's go back to the shower."

Hair a mass of foaming bubbles, shampoo running down our laughing faces, we shared the shower and apologised.

"Hey, Jackie. I'm sorry."

"That's okay. Do you want to know a secret?"

"Yes."

"I'm glad you kissed me. I liked it."

"Fuckin' hell! Will you be my real friend?"

I sploshed a handful of soapy bubbles on his face and we rolled about laughing.

"Just friends, Chesty. Let's go and get dry." Filthy football gear in hand and wet towels around our bellies, we went to get dressed.

"You play a good game of football, Chesty," I said. "you should have been a professional."

"You must be dreaming! Would you like a drink?"

"Okay."

Chesty walked over to the canteen bar and brought two glasses of pop to our table. "Cheers, Jackie! Here's to our new friendship."

"Cheers!"

A couple of lads walked into the canteen, one with his arm on his friend's shoulder. "That's McDermot and his badgy."

"What's a badgy?" I asked.

"It means. . . badgy! That's the only word we have for it: special friend if you like, and yet. . . that's not quite right. Nothing else can explain it," he said mysteriously.

"Which one is McDermot?"

"The older boy." As the evening wore on, I noticed quite a few nice lads with arm about shoulder. Nobody seemed to mind about a couple of lads showing open affection for each other.

"I want you for my badgy, Jackie. I like you and I'll never let you down," said my new friend.

"You better introduce me to McDermot and his badgy. I don't understand all this," I said as Chesty pressed against my knee in a sexy way.

"Well, I'll explain it the best way I can, Jackie. If you're my badgy, then I'm your friend. I'll help you and protect you."

"I can look after myself, thanks. Does that mean you are my badgy also?"

"No. You're the badgy – I'm the guy with my arm around your shoulder! It means, 'Keep off! This one is mine!' "

"Call the other two over," I said, getting quite interested.

"No. Let's have another drink and meet them at the bar. I'll introduce you. Okay?" Chesty gave my knee another little nudge.

McDermot was a husky kid about sixteen and the lad with him was about my own age. His name was Peter and he looked like a dream.

"Hi Chesty!" said the big boy. "Who's the new kid?"

"His name's Jackie. We palled up because he sleeps next to me and he's a fuckin' good football player. We play for the section," he said proudly.

McDermot squeezed his badgy's shoulder and the lovely boy looked up into his eyes adoringly.

I shook hands with young Peter. "You're Chesty's pal," he said. "Chesty is the best horseman in the whole battery. Lots of kids have a spur on their shoulder, but he's got a silver one."

"So have I!" said McDermot.

Two other lads came into the canteen, all pink faced and smiling. One had his arm around his badgy, and they looked extremely happy and content. They were about the same age – fifteen, no more than that. They joined up with other kids and pretty soon everyone was laughing and singing. It was all good fine comradeship and seemed quite natural.

"You mustn't go with anyone else if you're going to be my badgy," said Chesty. "Make as many friends as you like and enjoy yourself, but spend all your free time with me and I'll do the same."

"The guys won't think I'm funny, will they?"

"What do you mean?" he asked.

"They won't think I'm a bum boy?"

"They might. What do you think of the guys you've seen so far?"

"They look like wonderful friends to me. I don't see anything wrong with them," I replied.

"Well, what do you say?"

"Put your arm around my shoulder Chesty. I want to be your friend."

So I became Chesty's badgy, and his firm young arm about my shoulder meant just that.

Everything is wonderful! I do not see the big ugly boots, the drab canvas suits and the rough woollen long-johns. I do not hear the harsh voices of the drill instructors, nor do I feel the aches and pains in the muscles of my body. I do not see the sweat and tears, for I am blinded by the dazzling beauty of my young companions.

I see only the wonderful rosy cheeks, the pearly white teeth, sparkling eyes and lovely hair. Delightful smiles are all around me, and the air is alive with happy laughter and gaiety. Music fills my ears, and the smell of chocolate biscuits and spearmint chewing-gum fills my youthful nostrils. Happy faces, wonderful songs, everywhere I turn – lovely boys with polished chin-straps, neat little britches, taut and tight and absolutely gorgeous.

The sheer beauty of the countryside, the galloping steeds, boots in the stirrups, bottoms raised from the polished leather saddle. Shiny swords, narrow-trousered officers, silver spurs, handsome faces. Gorgeous mounts and swishy tails. The canvas suits are cast aside and I see my companions running naked in the shower. They are beautiful and they fill my life with happiness.

When we awake in the mornings and make our way to the washrooms, I do not hear the lavatory flush, nor do I see the scum on the wash basin before me. I see boys with towels hanging from a stiffened penis, showing off and thinking it a great joke. However, I see more than a joke: I see the most exciting erections and beautiful bodies, twisty pubic curls, swinging testicles, fine muscles, rich red lips and taut little bottoms that send shivers of pleasure running over my skin. For I am a homosexual boy and I am in paradise!

Toby, in the cot opposite me, was a lovely kid, brown-eyed, curly haired and always smiling. I was very horny for a boy like him.

He watched as I stripped naked for bed. "I bet you're going to have a wank," he said, winking.

"I am not! But I bet you are. . . sexy little bugger!"

Toby pulled the covers from his firm young body. All the kids in the room started laughing as he pulled away at his erection. "Put it away, Toby! It hasn't even got any hairs on yet!" A couple of kids in flying shirt-tails jumped on his bed, and a kind of sexy wrestling match took place: bare bums, fat little pigeons, legs and bellies all rubbing together, stroking, pushing, pink healthy cheeks aglow and eyes sparkling with boyish mischief.

"Cut it out!" said a stern voice from the doorway. "Get into bed! Monkeys, bloody little monkeys. . ."

The kids scattered and dived into their beds, all flushed and giggly.

"Goodnight, sir!" came the boyish chorus.

"Goodnight, boys. Two minutes to lights out. No more nonsense now!" It was all so friendly. . . I was very happy.

Five minutes in the darkness came the sound of a boy padding barefoot for a pee in the nearby toilets. Five more minutes brought two more peeing boys, the sweet notes of the final trumpet on the air and the boyish sounds of a restless young soldier. Then followed utter silence save the rustle of the trees in the cool night breeze.

"Hey Jackie. . ." a voice whispered in my ear.

I didn't answer.

"Are you awake, Jackie?" came Chesty's whispered voice. "Answer me!" He slid in beside me and placed one arm along the pillow. "Jackie?" he whispered softly.

I moved a little and placed my sleepy head on his nice warm arm.

"Please answer me. . ." His wonderful throbbing young dickie, hard and demanding, pressed against my bottom like a bar of steel. I sighed with pleasure, snuggled my head further along his muscular arm and felt the golden hair at his belly tickling me.

"I know you're not asleep! Answer me or I'll stick it up your bum!"

"Mmmm!" I sighed sleepily.

"It's going up. . . Whew! You happy with me, kid?" asked my panting lover.

"Yes," I whispered. "Don't leave me when you've finished. Stay and give a couple of hugs and kisses."

"You've a lovely bum, Jackie. . . a lovely sexy piece of bum!"

"Don't leave me. . ."

"I won't, badgy boy – I won't leave you. Shush! I haven't finished yet. Say something nice to me. . ."

"I like being your badgy. . ."

"A few minutes yet – I'm a horny bastard, ain't I?"

"Yes. Don't go. . . Stay and cuddle. I think you're lovely too."

"Badgy boy. . . I'm spunking up!"

"Shush!!! Not so loud, Chesty. . ."

"Keep still, Jackie boy. . . over now. . . finished. You enjoy it?"

"Kiss me and I'll whisper in your ear," I said happily.

Chesty enjoyed a nice kiss and a cuddle just as much as I. He was gentle and affectionate, whispered words of love and acted sweet and feminine in my arms. However, he was the masculine one and because he was the older and no doubt wished to assert his masculinity, placed his strong young arm about my shoulder everywhere we went. "Hands off! This one's mine."

We lived in our own little world, and after the day's duties and different lessons were finished, there were no adults around to wave an admonishing finger. They left us to ourselves. Most of the relationships between badgy and friend were harmless. None of the kids seemed to care about things like that. I think almost every one of them had a close and dear friend, but not many had the courage to show it openly with an arm around his shoulder.

Boxing was part of the training programme. All the kids hated it because it was compulsory. It didn't matter how good you were, or if you were inexperienced or not. You got thrown in the ring with a kid from another section and there was nothing you could do about it. The boxing instructors put kids of equal weight in the ring together and that was the only consideration shown.

We sat around the ring in gym shorts and vest: skinny kids, fat kids, farmer's lads and city boys. Chesty had his arm around my shoulder and I had a towel around my neck. They threw me in with a big husky broken-nosed kid, as brown as a pickled walnut and shiny with oil. One or two kissing noises came my way from the older boys who knew the score, and a few words from Chesty: "Take a dive! Take a dive, Jackie! He's a bastard and knocks everyone out!"

"I wanna gum shield!" I shouted.

"We ain't got one!" said the instructor.

"If you want me to box, I want a gum shield."

"What the hell for?"

"Because I like my teeth," I said, blushing like a schoolgirl.

"For Christ's sake, get on with it, kid," said a red-faced bombardier, stuffing some other lad's gum shield in my mouth and seating me on a little corner stool.

The moment the bell sounded, Darkie came at me like an express train but I wasn't there! When he turned around he walked into a straight left that shook him, and all the kids cheered. "Go on, Scouse! Let the bastard have it!"

He lost his cool and walked into a couple more straight lefts. My long reach gave me a slight advantage, and I was much taller and boxed English orthodox style. Darkie's jabs,

feints, ducks and professional know-how were all show-off!
He must have been watching too many movies, and
probably won his fights by scaring the other kids to death.
Anyway, he never laid a glove on me in the first round. In the
second round he came at me with a snarl on his face and his
eyes showing hatred, trying to put the frighteners on. I knew
all about this approach and my straight lefts brought the
claret streaming down from his nose.

Blood meant the end of a round, so the bell went and they
washed him down. The third round meant the end of a fight:
win, lose or draw. This time I pulled my punches without
touching him and he dropped his guard for a second, feeling
confused. That was all I needed: two dirty jabs in his short
ribs brought his head down and I butted him between the
eyes, my back to the referee. I poked my thumb in the kid's
eye and flattened him with a right cross to the jaw.

"Fuckin' 'ell!" said Chesty. "I thought you were a fairy!
Where did you learn to fight like that?"

"My old man taught me!" I lied. "He's a copper in
Liverpool."

"Jesus! You'll have to watch out, or they'll have you in the
boxing team."

I offered him my gloved hands. "Take them off for me,
Chesty. What's a fairy anyway?"

"Don't you know?" he asked. "You must have heard about
fairies!"

"Not really," I said.

"A fairy. . . a puff! A guy who sleeps with other guys."

"I thought they were homosexuals."

"Homo what?"

"Forget about it, Chesty. Let's watch the fights."

"What do you think of my badgy?" asked Chesty later that
night in the canteen. He had his arm round my shoulder as
usual, and was addressing his mates.

"Fuckin' good fight," said someone.

"He's lovely!" said Chesty, kissing me on the cheek in
front of them. I just laughed and blushed scarlet.

"Don't be naughty," I said shyly. "What will the guys
think?"

Someone rumpled my hair and smiled at me. "I know what
I think. I wish you were my badgy. . ."

Christmas, and the sound of sleighbells from the radio. . .
The world was white with snow and Christmas carols filled
the air. All the kids were excited and ready to go home on
Christmas leave. I stood before the six foot dressing mirror at
the entrance to our quarters and admired my riding britches,
polished boots and brightly burnished spurs that gleamed
like silver and made a clanking sound as I walked. Unfortunately my thick black curls had been shortened but my
cheeks were pink and fresh, and I thought I made a
handsome soldier boy in my dashing uniform.

Chesty sneaked up behind me and pinched my bottom.
"Hi, Jackie! Gee! You look great. Are you going to come to
the Isle of Wight with me? My mother says it'll be okay."

"Hell, why not? I don't want to go to Liverpool!" I said. I
could picture my mother walking into the pawnshop with
my shiny steel spurs and the medals I'd won for boxing and
hurdling.

We had planned to bathe together that afternoon: lock
ourselves in a bathroom and make love beneath the warm
soapy water. I could hardly wait for the final parade when we
would be inspected and, providing we passed muster and
satisfied the eagle eye of the B.S.M., allowed to proceed on
leave the next morning.

"I'll be glad to go home with you, Chesty. Thanks for being
so kind," I whispered as we sneaked half-naked into the
bathroom.

"You'll love it!" he said, turning the taps to fill up the big
tub and removing the towel from his trim waist. "I live in
Freshwater village, a house called Hazelbush Cottage, and
it's miles from anywhere. My old man has two hunters in his
stable and we can go riding every day."

The sight of my handsome friend and his magnificent
naked brown body made me say, "What about the nights?
Will we ride by night, Chesty?"

He grabbed me and we jumped into the warm water.
"Wait till we get home, Jackie! We'll be sleeping in a big
double bed and we won't have to hide away like this when I
make love to you."

I could hardly wait for him to take me in his arms, kiss me,
call me a beautiful boy and thrill me beneath the soapy water
with his springy and tensile penis.

"Jackie. . . Jackie. . . You're fuckin' lovely! Don't you ever want to do this to me?" asked my driving seducer.

"You're enjoying yourself, aren't you?" I replied.

"Jesus! I'm in heaven! I was just thinking about you, that's all."

"Just kiss me, Chesty. . . Kiss me and say nice things to me. Tell me you love me."

"You know I do. . . Wow! I'm going to come in a minute."

"Well, say you love me!"

"I love you! I love you! I'm coming! Jesus! I'm filling you with love!"

We washed and I comforted him until one of our friends knocked at the door. "The bombardier is on his way over, Chesty. Have you got Jackie in there with you?"

"Yeah!"

"Well, get him outta there. I've filled the tub next door for you." It was the gorgeous creature who had rumpled my hair in the canteen. I slipped naked into the other tub, throwing my towel and slippers on the floor.

"You kids all right in here?" said the red-faced bombardier.

"Yes sir."

"Well, don't leave the place in a mess. There will be no one about to clean up after you." He marched away as if he owned the goddamn world and Chesty went out with him, swinging dickie showing limp, thick and hefty against the damp towel about his waist.

"Let me jump in with you, Jackie?" His name was Paul and I liked him.

"What for?"

"Christ, you know what for!" He slipped out of his knickers and locked the door. Paul was a real beauty and I wanted him as much as he wanted me.

"What if Chesty finds out?"

"Forget about Chesty. Can I jump in with you?"

"If you want to, Paul – just don't tell anyone. If my mate finds out he'll go potty."

"Fuckin' 'ell, Jackie – you're lovely. Can I bum you?"

"Well, if you like me all that much. . ."

"Wow! You're a real bum boy! I like you, Jackie. . . Get on your knees."

I wanted to make the handsome boy happy, so I took him in my arms first and kissed him lightly on the lips.

"Wow!" he said, kissing me gently on the forehead. "You're just like a girl. Will you be my badgy?"

"You're a nice guy, Paul, but I belong to Chesty. Get a fuckin' move on will you? It's my turn next and I haven't had a nice bit of bum for months!" I said excitedly.

Paul got as good as he gave, and he walked from the bath-house blowing kisses. Poking the gorgeous young Brighton boy had done something to me: created a change in my desires and made me horny for a sweet little boy.

There was not much time left unfortunately before we all went on leave. The boy I really fancied was the youngster who slept opposite me: Toby, the kid who played with his dickie in front of the others.

"Why don't you get someone else to do that for you?" I said. "It's a lot more fun when your friend does it."

"Do you do it with Chesty?" asked the kid.

"What do you think?" I replied, getting very horny for him.

"I think you're Chesty's bum boy. I see you in bed together and wank over you," he admitted.

"Chesty's not like that. We just have a cuddle sometimes when I get homesick. Come for a walk round the stables with me, Toby. We're all going off in the morning and I won't see you for almost a month." I put my arm around the lovely young virgin's shoulder as we walked beneath the shadows of the old stables.

"You want me for your badgy, do you Jackie?" asked the cutie.

"What would you say if I did?" I asked, giving his shoulder a friendly little squeeze and getting more horny by the minute.

"I'll let you know when the holidays are over," he said, giggling like a schoolboy. "You're making me horny."

"You're always horny, Toby."

"So are you."

"I'm horny for you! Come in the stable and I'll show you."

We climbed up onto a pile of hay in the empty building. It was quite dark and impossible to be disturbed in the old place which was due for demolition.

"Are you going to pull it for me, Jackie?" asked the boy.

"Do you want me to?"

"Yes," said gentle Toby, unfastening his trousers.

"Will you play with mine?" I asked him nicely.

"I don't mind. Should we take our trousers off and do it in the nude like you and Chesty do? I watch you so don't deny it!"

"If you take your trousers off, Toby, I'll be up you."

"Like Chesty gets up you every night?" said Toby, pulling his pigeon.

"Yes, you sexy little spy! Get your pants off! Have you done it before?"

"Not up my bum. Only between my legs. Chesty pulled me off and tried to shove his cock up me but it wouldn't go in."

"This one will go in, Toby, but don't tell anybody. Promise?"

"Okay," he whispered. "I'm ready for you now. Will you suck it for me? I won't say a word to anyone."

"My mouth might wander a little. . . That sweet bum of yours looks kissable." Toby enjoyed my searching tongue, gasped with unexpected pleasure when it entered him, and wriggled with delight.

"Finish it off, Jackie! Suck me till I come!"

"Wait until I get this up you, Toby. You'll enjoy it better. Don't get too excited. I'll suck you off afterwards."

My favourite position: a lovely young creature on his back looking into my eyes and my dickie ready to enter him.

"Do you want it right up?"

"Whoo! I'm almost spunking off just looking at it. Get up me! I can't be a virgin all my life."

"How's that?" I whispered, giving him my meat.

"It hurts!" protested the curly haired virgin.

"It won't hurt for long. Stop playing with your dick – I'll do that in a couple of minutes. You're a sweet kid. I'm surprised no one has been up you before now. . . Any better?"

"Bang away, Jackie! Fucking hell!"

"I'm going to spunk up! Ready? I'm almost there! Wow! You've got it, Toby – you're not a virgin any more!" It was all good happy sex. Toby was willing so he must have wanted it all the time.

"Will you visit me every night after Chesty has been up you?" Toby's voice was movingly sincere.

"Yes. I'll stick it up you every night. Is that what you want?"

"And a suck!" said the friendly beauty, no longer sweet and pure.

"Okay. Let's get dressed. Do you like being bummed?" I asked jokingly.

"Fabulous! Hey, Jackie – boys can't get a baby can they?" Sweet Toby was older than me!

"I don't know, Toby, but if they can then you are well and truly pregnant!" I said, laughing at his innocence.

"Have you fucked Chesty?" asked the nosy young devil.

"No. I'm going to have a good try though. I'm going home with him tomorrow. How do I know you won't talk about all this?"

Toby buttoned up his pants and thought for a few seconds.

"I could be your friend, Jackie. I think about you a hell of a lot. Do you really like me or was it just a bit of bum?"

"I care for you. I'd kiss you if I thought you'd like it," I said.

"Would you cut your wrist for me?" asked the lad.

"You're a crazy kid! Blood brothers? You mean it?"

"Sure. It's better than kissing. I'll use my spur. I'll keep word and always be your comrade," said Toby.

"Fuck it! Let's do it with a razor. We'll do it in the washroom in case you fuckin' bleed to death," I said.

Chesty came along for the performance and a few more kids gathered around. "What the fuckin' hell's going on?" asked a big ginger-haired boy with a Scottish accent and the biggest pair of swinging testicles in the universe.

"Toby and Jackie are cutting their wrists."

"Crazy bastards!"

We cut the wrists and drank each other's blood. Toby came back to me in the middle of the night, creeping into my bed and putting his arms around me.

"What is it, Toby?"

"When we get back off leave, will you walk arm in arm with me? Both of us? My arm around you, and yours around me? I haven't got a real friend. Will you, Jackie?"

"I'm your brother, ain't I?"

"You're more than that. You can kiss me now," said the fine young soldier boy.

Things were getting a bit complicated. I wanted to be Chesty's boy *and* Toby's man. They both moved me and I felt all mixed up. I tried to talk about it with Chesty when we were on the Southampton train and bound for the Isle of Wight ferry. Unfortunately, he was too excited. . .

CHAPTER ELEVEN

The Three Musketeers

I couldn't understand how anyone could get so worked up about going home: the army was my home now and I loved it! The food was marvellous and the warm uniforms looked dashing! There were clean sheets on the beds and real blankets, workouts in the gym, riding every day, swimming, football, a handsome husky big boy who loved me and a young beauty who wanted me to love him: my blood brother. . . What more could I ask?

Hazelbush Cottage, Freshwater village – the name sounded beautiful and the house looked as if it had been the one chosen for all the Christmas cards in the shop windows.

I loved it the moment I set eyes on the picturesque country farmhouse: thatched roof, quaint old-fashioned windows with bull's-eye glass, snow-topped young trees in the garden and robin redbreasts pecking away at the breadcrumbs on the window sills.

His parents made me welcome, and the two hunters in the stable pricked up their ears when I stroked these magnificent animals. I could hardly wait to saddle up and go galloping over the snow-covered countryside. His mother showed us to the room we were to share, fished out some clothes that her big handsome son had grown out of and threw them on the huge double bed.

"I suppose you'll want to get out of your uniforms," she said. Alan has plenty of things. Try some of these on, lad."

She held a pair of cavalry twill trousers up to my waist. "They should fit you, dear," she said.

Chesty seemed to take everything for granted. He didn't realise how lucky he was, but he wasn't a mummy's darling by any means.

"Let's dress exactly the same," he said, "then we'll go for a

159

ride through the village."

I felt quite rich in the cavalry twill, bright red shirt and gorgeous fawn pullover. We saddled up and off we went, scattering the squawking chickens, frightening the waddling ducks and waving at the pretty village girls. It was terrific and made me feel quite masculine. I felt at home in the saddle and was proud of my control. The snow-covered countryside almost made my head reel with its grandeur and magnificent beauty. The animals beneath our sturdy legs seemed to know every colourful picturesque spot. They soared across the frosty hedgerows and enjoyed the journey as much as their young riders.

A mouth-watering dinner awaited us on our return and the conversation at the table was pleasant and homely.

"What do you think of the army, Jackie?" asked the old man, passing me a dish of garden peas shiny with melted butter. "Do you like it as much as Alan does?"

"Great!" I said. "I love it. Anything is better than Liverpool."

"That's what my son said before he left home," replied the old man.

"Well, Jackie's right, dad. A lad gets bored at home and the army is exciting! We may get shipped out to Aden in the spring!" He jumped up and performed a childish war dance around the table. "Wooo-ooo-ooo. The Gulf of Aden! The white man's grave! Oooooo-woo-oo-wo-wo-wo-wo-wo. . . White man's grave!"

"Sit down, you silly bugger!" said his dad.

"Sorry, dad, but it's true. We might be going to Aden," said Chesty.

His father looked across at me. "What do you think about that, young man?" he enquired.

"I don't care if we go to Timbuktoo! I love the army," I replied with my mouth full.

"You're only children," said the old man. "There's fighting taking place all over the British Empire. Trouble in the East. Riots in India, Palestine and God knows where else. You don't know what's going to happen to you."

"We'll be alright. We've got good comrades. . ."

"Children, bloody children! You're only kids!" He fished out a flagon of red wine and we sat around talking like grown up men.

Perhaps it was the effect of the heady wine we'd drunk, or maybe the intimacy of sharing a lovely warm room in private for the first time... Cheeks all flushed with pleasure, lips parted and body tingling with excitement, I watched my friend undress. He was a man. There was no doubt about that! "You look like a young lion!" I said.

Chesty smiled, thumped his big brown chest and said, "Me Tarzan! You Jane!" He certainly looked like Tarzan: thick, golden hair covered his handsome head, bright blue eyes sparkled, and a huge long sexual organ hung heavy from its mass of twisty pubic hair. His fat round testicles swung heavy with seed and a delight to the eye.

"Take your knickers off," he said. "I want to have a real good look at you." This was the first time we'd been so close and safe. "You are really beautiful! You've got eyes and skin like a girl."

"I thought you didn't like girls," I said as if I didn't know.

"I don't. I like you. Take your knickers off."

It was the nakedness that brought us to life; my knickers fell to the carpet and we just looked at each other. His great thick dickie grew longer and the shiny head peeped at me from its moving, delicate hood of skin. It just kept on growing and thickening until it reached its full length and the big fat shiny head was free and glistening.

"You're a handsome bastard, Chesty," I said. "You're a man!"

"You're a beautiful boy. I love looking at you. Turn around. I want to see you from the back," said my friend.

"You see it every bloody night!"

"I don't see it like this. It's usually dark and when we go to make love in the bath-house I don't have time to admire you. I could eat you all up!"

My own pigeon was standing up good and stiff but it was nothing compared to my friend's manly penis. "Do you like me from the front?" I said. "Do you think I'll get a great big one like yours when I'm older?"

"Mine was like that when I fourteen," he said. "You've got a nice one and you have a neat shiny black bush. Don't worry about it. Anyway, what difference does it make? You never bum anybody with it."

"I do. I bummed young Toby last night: stuck it right up him and filled him with rice pudding," I boasted.

"Wow!" said Chesty. "I've bummed about seven boys in our room but I couldn't get it up Toby. What's he like? Did he enjoy it?"

"Why do you think we cut our wrists?"

"Toby's a dreamer. He's like you; always thinking about heroes and fuckin' battlefields. Do you love him?"

"I know I do. I can love you both, can't I?"

Chesty opened his arms wide. "Come to me," he said, like Jesus calling the sinners to his outstretched arms. I fell into an embrace with him and slowly slid to my knees.

"I'm going to show how much I really love you."

"Wow! I never thought you would suck it for me"

I stood up. "I'll do everything you want, Chesty."

He enjoyed my lips around his masculine throbbing flesh and the searching tongue near his bottom. "Kiss me there, Jackie. I love it. More. . . more! Put your tongue right inside. Wow!"

Loving and cuddling, kissing every tiny spot and bringing him to a mad desire gave me more pleasure than anything I could dream of.

"Don't get jealous when I start going with Toby. I want him for my friend."

"We can be the Three Musketeers. Me an' you 'n' Toby. I won't get jealous. Suck it, Jackie."

"Here goes!"

Chesty discovered how much I really cared. . .

The holiday at an end, we returned to the depot to find all the kids milling around in the canteen, seeking the friends they'd been parted from and glad to get back among the fine young soldier boys. Toby was there. I went straight to him and put my arm around his shoulder. "Hi, Toby!"

"Hi, Jack! Can I put my arm around you?"

"We're brothers, ain't we?"

Toby loved it, and so did I.

All the boys had some special quality, something going for them that made them stand out. Chesty was a powerful horseman and strived to gain the rough-rider's badge. I shone at athletics and boxing. Some were fine musicians and sought the badge of the silver trumpet. Toby had a special magic. He was the son of a vet, a horse doctor who had almost reared his child in the saddle. The boy could do anything with a horse; they just gentled at his touch.

The boys in the barrack room laughed at him in a friendly way, because he was the only one who still remained hairless about his pubic region. When it came to horseflesh, however, the boy was in a different class altogether. They called him Tom Mix in the rodeo: Tom Mix, the greatest cowboy and horseman in the world. Animals which even the biggest boys were scared of didn't worry fearless young Toby. He'd run a gentle hand over the whip-marked flank, whisper softly in the horse's ear and climb aboard. His mere presence calmed the nervous creature, and the boys really admired him for this.

"How do you do it?" I asked him.

"Love, kindness, I don't know really. It just comes natural. I talk to them, understand them. They know me, know that I love them. They're just like people to me. I can tell if they are not feeling well or if they are unhappy. . . they talk to me, Jackie."

Everybody knew about his magic touch with horses and he wore the silver spur with pride.

"You'll have to teach me."

"I'll try, Jackie. I'll introduce you to the scary ones, help you in the arena and jump alongside you when the going gets tough. You can help me in the boxing ring. What do you say?"

"What can I say? We're brothers, ain't we? Show me your scar."

He pulled back his sleeve and we stared at the scarred wrists, Toby full of pride and joy. "We'll always be brothers, Jack. We might need each other some day. We could find ourselves fighting in Afghanistan, or India. What about the white man's grave? You'll need a trusty comrade there! You don't think it's silly, do you?"

"No, I can see you coming to my rescue, Toby – jumping your horse over the dead bodies and mounted guns, and saving my life in some faraway country."

"You'll do the same for me, Jack. I know you will!"

Chesty walked in on us. "What! Are you two silly buggers

still playin' fuckin' soldiers? Let's get a round of drinks! We'll have pints this time. Come and stand by the bar. Hey there! Three pints of ginger beer please."

"One for all! And all for one!" shouted Toby. It meant so much to brave young Toby.

The kids called us The Three Musketeers, because we were always together and always singing, "The horse platoon. . . the horse platoon. . . the thundering hooves of the horse platoon. . ."

It was a heap of fun. We were growing up together, getting closer with each passing night: Chesty loving me and Toby creeping to my warm bed after Chesty had kissed me goodnight. We were snuggled close one night, his fingers in my hair and stiff little wand in my lips. "Hey, you two," said a boyish voice. "Watch out! The bombardier is coming this way! I saw him through the window." Too late! Heavy footsteps at the doorway. We froze! A voice said, "Everybody sound asleep? Goodnight boys. . ." No flashing torch, no sneaky footsteps in the night – just the friendly voice saying goodnight. . .

"Carry on, Jackie. The night man's gone. Suck it till it comes!"

Being in bed with Chesty or my sweet friend Toby was absolutely divine. But one day I got a nasty kick while playing football and finished up in the military hospital just a few hundred yards away.

I was almost fifteen at the time. Lying in bed, I was missing my mates from the band and drums and feeling a bit sad. It was a lonely place. No boys, friends or smiling, happy faces. Chesty and Toby would be having fun, I thought. "I'll be glad when I get out of this bloody place."

The sun streamed through the window and the night nurse leaned over my bed. "You can get up today, kid!" He was a very handsome guy: dark shiny hair and gold tooth that glittered when he smiled. His hair was thick and wavy, and shone like silk. His breath was fresh and fragrant and his eyes a sparkling blue; kind eyes with dancing little devils in them.

"Take it easy on that leg," he said. "You'll be okay. No bones broken."

He threw a suit of hospital blues on my locker and gave me

an enormous scarlet-coloured handkerchief. Why scarlet? The same reason as the blankets: blood. Blood and broken bones are part of the soldier's pay. You might wake up in a blood-stained bandage and accept it, but you could die of shock if you awoke on a white blanket and discovered a pool of blood.

The bright blue suit is the uniform of the hospitalised soldier. Rank means nothing: patients, mere patients in the hands of the dedicated nurse. Adam was dedicated. He came to me and washed my hair in the shower.

Towel around my waist, I hobbled back to my bed and donned a snow-white shirt. It was quite a simple act but struggling into my tight gym-knickers was very difficult because I couldn't bend my knee.

"Holy Jesus!" I complained, falling back on the white counterpane. "I'm a fucking cripple!"

A big husky guy from the Cameronians came over. "What's up, kid? Having trouble?" He grabbed my knickers and pulled them up around my bottom.

"Thanks."

"Think nothing of it," he said, rumpling my hair. "Anytime, kid. Just say the word!"

Slippers on, a few paces around the bed. It would soon improve with a little exercise. Brush and comb in hand, I made my way to the wash-room and admired myself in the mirror. Such vanity: scarlet sash, bright blue pants, snow-white shirt and jet black hair. I loved myself!

The husky Cameronian came waltzing in. "Badgy," he said, smiling at me. "I'll give you a game of snooker." He was a friendly kind of guy, handsome as hell, blond as a Norwegian, powerful as Tarzan with hands like an Irishman's spade. Big, real big and sexy.

I limped along the white-tiled corridors, with Husky leading the way, the wind rustling the tall green trees, outside blossom flying through the open windows, a smell of springtime and new life in my nostrils, chunks of bubble-gum in my chomping jaws.

"What *are* you eating?" asked Husky.

"Bubblegum. Peach flavour. Wanna bit?"

"Fuckin' bubblegum!" he said scornfully. "What kinda fuckin' soldier are you?"

"A boy soldier. I'm stationed just a few hundred yards down the road."

"Get a fuckin' move on!" he said with a laugh. "You ain't paralysed." He pinched my bottom. I giggled, so he pinched it again as we entered the recreation room. The continuous movement around the table seemed to ease the stiffness in my knee, so we played after lunch, went for a stroll in the grounds and played another few games of snooker in the evening.

Long hair is not accepted in the army. I needed a haircut, so Husky gave me a pot of Brylcreem.

"Use this," he said, leaving the pot on my locker top. "Did you enjoy the snooker?"

At this particular moment, I was busy with a giant bubble but it burst all over my freckled nose.

"Bubblegum soldiers!" snorted Husky, and strode off to his bed.

Adam made the rounds, tucked me in and went about his night duties. With the smell of hospital in my nose, a small dim light above a desk and the sound of some unfortunate bastard in pain, sleep was just creeping up on me when I heard a quiet voice in my ear. "Move over, kid."

"Why?"

"I'm lonely," said my husky friend. "Can I get in bed with you?"

I was feeling kind of lonely myself, so I moved over expecting a friendly sexual encounter with Husky's enormous penis which was already poking from his shorts. He slid in beside me, pulled my knickers off, slapped some Brylcreem on me and shoved his great big sexual organ hard up my bottom.

"Leave me alone!" I said. "Piss off or I'll call the night nurse!"

"Shut up! We'll get into trouble if you make a noise."

It was one great wrestling match and I didn't enjoy it at all. No tender kiss, no sweet caress, no fond endearments in my lonely ear – nothing. Just a pair of heavy hands holding me down and a pair of hairy testicles banging against my bottom. No wonder he gave me the Brylcreem for a present. Talk about Greeks bearing gifts! Some gift!

"There!" he said at last, hard home, all the way. "There, there, Badgy boy. All over. Shush! Go to sleep."

Badgy, the word I thought meant special friend and only used among my young companions, turned out to be army slang. It meant "fresh meat, chicken!"

It was the first time anyone had actually bummed me without my permission and it left me feeling a bit tearful and sad. I suppose I enjoyed it, but it didn't seem fair and I was still horny.

"Miserable devil," I said to myself. "He could have had the decency to give me a little pull or something. . ." Toby kept coming into my thoughts and I just had to play with myself for a few minutes until at last I fell asleep with a sticky mess on my belly

The sweet tones of a silver trumpet came melodiously to my ears and brought me to my senses. It was springtime and the smell of blossom came through the open windows, mingling with the medicinal hospital smell and filling the ward with a strange and beautiful fragrance.

Blue-clad patients began to move about the ward and the night nurse was on his rounds: taking the temperature of the very sick, asking his routine questions, feeling pulse beats and watching the movements of the patients' chests to check their respiration. The familiar sound of spur-clad boots made me look towards the door. It was young Toby. He looked around the ward. I knew he would never spot me because the lines of snow-white beds and blue woolly dressing-gowns all looked the same. I gave him a wave and shouted, "Here! Over here!"

A big broad grin spread over his delightful young face and he marched down the ward with his spurs clanking. "Hi, Jackie," he said. "I've brought some comics for you. I'm not supposed to be in here really – visiting times don't permit but I came anyway. How are you getting on?"

"I'm doing fine," I replied. "I was on my feet all day yesterday, so I should be out soon. Nothing's broken, just a badly bruised bone."

"Do you want the bad news?" asked the night nurse, not waiting for a reply. He shoved the screens around my bed. "You better get out of here, sonny. If the matron sees you tearing the arse out of her polished floor with those spurs, she'll have your balls off. Go on! Get out of here!"

Toby threw the comics on my bed, said "cheerio" and marched away blushing scarlet.

"Who was that?" asked the night nurse, fitting the last screen into position.

"My brother."

"He should come during visiting hours," the nurse said quietly. "How's the knee?" he asked, pulling the covers from me and exposing my morning erection.

"A bit stiff," I replied, covering the bean-stalk with my hand. "Sorry. I always wake up like this."

Warm talcum in his powdery palms, Adam massaged my knee. "Don't be embarrassed," said his gentle voice. "I've seen everything. It's quite natural for a healthy lad. Turn over and try to bend the knee."

Firm hands at my leg, stiffened penis rubbing at the blankets, bottom exposed to Adam's twinkling eyes, all kinds of sexy thoughts ran through my head. The knee wouldn't bend, so he slipped an elastic bandage over it, slapped my bottom and turned me on my back.

"How's that?" he asked.

"Much better. Thank you."

He teased my hair with his fingers. "Who was at your bed last night?"

"No one."

"I saw a big guy talking to you after lights out."

"Just saying goodnight," I replied, smiling into his handsome face, eyes a-flutter and giving away all my secrets.

Adam slipped off the bandage. "I'm going to bathe you," he said quietly. "Is that alright with you?"

"If you like me," lips parted, penis throbbing. . .

He kissed my cheek, made me blush and threw a robe over my shoulders. "Come along. I'm going to put you in the tub."

"What will the other guys think?"

"Nothing," replied Adam. "I bathe everybody. It's my job."

He certainly enjoyed his work – fingers searching everywhere, kisses at my soapy belly, gentle hands at my testicles, kisses on the lips and boyish nipples.

"You're a sweet kid," he said affectionately. "I think we're going to be good friends, don't you?"

No shrinking violet, Adam wore a decoration for bravery on his chest. Like most male nurses, the milk of human kindness ran through his veins. Obviously, he was one of my own kind, cared for me and was prepared to let the relationship develop naturally. Our morning routine was indeed beautiful. No longer shy, I lay beneath his tender hands, kisses at my nakedness, fingers grasping my youthful erection, lips meeting as the seed shot high and landed on my bare brown chest.

It got more beautiful and exciting as the days passed; on my belly, Adam's stroking hands at my shoulders, my bottom, kisses in the most intimate spot until I could stand it no more.

"Do it!" I said excitedly. "Make love to me!"

"Tonight," he said quietly. "Is that what you really want?"

"Yes. Fuck me! Please, Adam. I can't wait any longer."

We sealed it with a loving kiss. Ah well, it *was* springtime!

Patients were given all kinds of daily jobs: polishing the gleaming wooden floors, cleaning windows and tending the flower beds. The simple chores were therapeutic. Medical orderlies were available for cleaning duties but the eagle-eyed Matron missed nothing. She realised the patients needed therapy and put the men to work. The guy who swung the twenty-pound bumper was indeed polishing the floors but also building up his wasted muscle tissue, just as the guy in the garden was filling his lungs with the clean fresh air they required.

My morning duties sent me walking all over the hospital, in and out of the wards and offices, changing flowers, cleaning out the waste-paper baskets and putting a tiny shovel of coal on the Matron's fire.

Strange things happened. "Piss in this bottle for me?" asked one guy.

"Why? What the hell for?"

"Don't ask fucking questions. Piss in the bottle!"

It had his name on it, so I pissed in it every morning. He was seeking a clean fresh specimen of urine and an early release. Medicine was still in its infancy. Guys exchanged specimens of blood and samples of saliva and actually paid cash for an infected blood or tubercular spit.

Some guys would do anything to get out of the army. The

discipline in the Brigade of Guards was frightening! Young Guardsmen jumped from their barrack-block windows, broke their legs and actually committed suicide. Other men, of course, would rather die than quit. Heroes, malingerers, the weak and the strong; it takes all kinds to make an army.

Adam's parting gift was truly romantic, a work of cunning craftsmanship. There were about ten or twelve patients in the ward, and Adam ensured that they slept soundly by the simple methods at his disposal. He slipped them a mickey, which, in the colourful vernacular of our American cousins, means a strong sedative.

The curtained compartment was our boudoir, the love nest where we could bill and coo and kiss and share endearments. Adam went in search of Aladdin's cave. Abracadabra! Open Sesame! The handsome charmer used his magic wand, entered the forbidden territory, overpowering, tantalising and leaving his precious jewels in the richness of the cavern.

Sound as a bell, I was back with my mates, swimming and getting my body back into working shape again. Chesty was back in my bed, Toby in my arms and love in my life.

"Let's always keep our sleeves rolled up," suggested Toby, full of boyish romantic thoughts. "Then we'll be able to look at our scars any time we like without having to ask. . ."

Teardrops on My Drum

The stick can beat a rat-a-tat-tat, but if the drum is taut and pigskin tightly stretched, even the sound of a raindrop on it can be heard. It goes pit-a-pat, pit-a-pat. . .

The band and drums paraded, full dressed in all their gleaming colour: scarlet trimmings, golden filigree, gleaming brass and white cockades. Instruments of shining silver; beautiful, beautiful big trombones, gorgeous drums all white and crested, glittering french horns, gleaming cymbals, polished flutes of black and silver, kettledrums, side-drums laced with snow-white rope, silver music stands, neat and tiny, clipped to firm young forearms, huge music stands on tripods, cornets and horns of every shape and size made up the big parade.

Spur-clad, pink-faced boys in britches formed a military square. Flags and bunting, polished leather riding boots, shimmering with ankle chain, beautifully groomed horses – swishy-tailed and testy, moustachioed young officers and one great, glorious-looking tall drum-major completed the colourful spectacle.

A powerful, stentorian voice rang out and carried across the waters of Southampton docks. Music, sweet music filled the air. Fine young chests, bursting with pride, filled out the shiny-buttoned tunics. Heads held high, golden lanyards at their arms, the band boys played a glorious tune.

I tapped my drum: rat-a-tat-tat. . .

A long spectacular row of handsome, slim, young silver trumpeters lined the quayside. Gorgeous triangular flags hung from the instruments at their lips. The band and drums played "Auld Lang Syne".

I tapped my drum: a-rat-a-rat-tat. . . and again. . . a-rat-a-tat-tat. . .

One boy with a silver trumpet wore a shining spur and a military cap upon his golden hair. His eyes were blue, his teeth gleamed white and his wonderful face was shiny bright... He waved to me, "So long, Jackie! So long, kid! So long, Jackie boy!!! See you in hell!!! So long...g!!!!"

"Should auld acquaintance be forgot"... a-rat-a-tat-tat... a-rat-a-tat-tat... The great white troopship sailed away taking Chesty with it and the band played on... a-rat-a-tat-tat... pit-a-pat, pit-a-pat... Chesty waved but I couldn't look any more... a-rat-a-tat-tat... pitter pitter pitter pat... Hold your head up, boy!!!... a-rat-a-tat-tat... Hold your head up! Soldiers can cry! It ain't against the regulations!... pit-a-pat... pitter pitter pitter pat... Out of Southampton harbour... out of sight now... a-rat-a-tat-tat... soldiers can cry... pitter pitter pitter pat... "For the sake of auld lang syne..."

The music stops.

"Fall out! The band and drums!"

"Dismiss the piquet line!"

"Break off! The military square!"

Goodbye, Chesty...

"Get them in the transport, Sergeant-Major!"

All aboard the steamy old railway train... polished boots and shiny chin-straps... instruments of every shape and size.

"What did you join the army for?" the singing began. "Why did you join the army? What did you join the army for? You must-a been fuckin' well barmy."

"I've been in the saddle for hours an' hours, stuck it as long as I could! Stuck it an' stuck it, until I said fuck it! My arsehole is not made of wood! Hi-jigi-jig, fuck a little pig, follow the band..."

"Fall in the band and drums! Strike up the band! March them back!"

A hundred marching boys came by
Swinging arms... heads held high
Golden lanyards... fine young chests
Proud hearts beating in their breasts.
Cornets trombones everywhere
Wonderful music filled the air...

The band played "Colonel Bogey"... a-rat-a-tat-tat...
"And the same to you... bollocks!!!... they make a fine
great stew!"

It made me feel proud and masculine. It sent shivers down
my spine and a great feeling of patriotism washing over me
like water. Clashing cymbals and rattling drums in my ear...
Maybe I will see Chesty again... a-rat-a-tat-tat... Soldiers
can cry... pit a pat... It ain't against the regulations... Chin
in! Chest out! Hold your silly head up, Jackie boy... You
might catch the next troopship... a-rat-a-tat-tat... "And the
same to you! Bollocks!!!... they make a fine great stew!"

Fifteen more years to go kid... You'll meet him some
place, some fuckin' place... a-rat-a-tat-tat... Hell! It ain't the
end of the ... pit-a-pat... fuckin' world! We can live... and
maybe die... a-rat-a-tat-tat... Fighting side by side...
"Don't put the lights on, Charlie... wait till I get him in
bed... an' grab 'is bollocks!!!... an' the same to you!" The
music makes my heart beat faster... I'm a fuckin' soldier
boy... pit-a-pat... I'm the fuckin' mighty British fuckin'
Empire!... "And the same to you! Bollocks! da-da-da
bollocks"... pitter pitter pitter pat... "They make a fine
great stew"... Toby will still be there, riding his silly
friggin'... pit-a-pat... horses... "And the same to you!" We
can die... in the white man's grave... me and lovely
Toby... a-rat-a-tat-tat... "And the same to you!!!"

Almost home now... I can hear the horse platoon... The
thundering thundering thundering hooves... head up,
Jackie boy... The thundering hooves of the horse platoon...
don't let Toby see you cry... he thinks you're a man, his
fuckin' hero... "Bollocks!... and the same to you!"...
a-rat-a-tat-tat... pitter pitter pitter pat!... Almost home!
Here we go! Hold your fuckin' head up high!... Thundering! Thundering! Right across the plain... a rat-a-tat-tat...
I'm a fuckin' soldier!

I can hear the horse platoon... the thundering hooves of
the horse platoon... and the pitter pat of the teardrops... on
my drum.

Jack's amazing life story continues in:

Jack and Jamie Go To War
by Jack Robinson

This second volume starts in 1937, with the fifteen-year-old hero back in his home town after his spell as a boy soldier. The action ranges from Liverpool under the Blitz through D-Day,, via New York, South Africa, and the Allied landings in Naples. It sees Jack as a wartime commando, then a seaman with the convoys, caught up in mutiny and racketeering, and always in pursuit of boys. *ISBN 0 85449 077 9*

Some other titles in our series of Memoirs by gay men are:

Flame: A Life On The Game
by Flame

The year is 1971, and working-class life holds little promise for 14-year-old Stephen as he waits to leave school. "I'm not going to stay around here working in a factory, honey. I'm going OUT THERE, where there's LIFE. I'm going to be a prostitute, just like my mum." So Stephen became Flame, and this is his true story.

"A raw, eloquent, social document" (*Guardian*).

ISBN 0 907040 23 3

Parallel Lives
by Peter Burton

Among the topics covered in this crowded memoir are the mod clubs of the 1960s; a teenage literary apprenticeship; collaborations with Robin Maugham; reminiscences of Gerald Hamilton ("Mr Norris") and Michael Davidson; touring with Rod Stewart; and the rise and fall of *Gay News*.

"As a social historian he is completely to be trusted. As a human being he is extremely sympathetic" (George Melly, *New Society*). "I am charmed by it" (*New York Native*).

ISBN 0 907040 65 9

The Erotic World of Peter de Rome

by Peter de Rome

This English film-maker, resident in America, won fame for his films described as "an elevated celebration of sex" (*Financial Times*).

Witty and adventurous, de Rome's own life reads like the screenplay for one of his films, taking him through the wartime RAF, New York in the 1950s, the Civil Rights movement in the Deep South, as well as the story of his movies.

"De Rome's racy literary style should ensure him a wide readership" (*Gay Times*).

ISBN 0 907040 46 2

and in our Gay Modern Classics series:

The Men With the Pink Triangle

by Heinz Heger

A unique personal testimony of the life and death of gay prisoners in the Nazi concentration camps, highly acclaimed on first publication and now re-issued.

"A moving example of the will to 'bear witness' on the part of people who survived the death camps" (*Times Literary Supplement*).

ISBN 0 907040 03 9 (pbk)
ISBN 0 85449 014 0 (cased)

GMP is the world's leading publisher of books of gay interest, with a wide range of titles including Fiction, History, Art, Photography, Health and Humour as well as Biography and Memoirs. Send for our full catalogue to GMP Publishers Ltd, P O Box 247, London N15 6RW, England.